This book is dedicated to my mother and father, wh  *d hard work, and to my wife Diane and my daughter* support.

B. Devine

I dedicate this book to all those people who want to experience, appreciate and preserve the unique natural resources of the U.S. Virgin Islands.

Toni Thomas

It is both my honor and pleasure to congratulate the staffs of the University of the Virgin Islands Conservation Data Center and Cooperative Extension Service on the completion of the Field Guide to the Plant and Marine Communities of the Virgin Islands. The many hours of arduous labor have resulted in a noteworthy publication that offers the reader many insights into the various ecosystems that may be found in the Territory. I am sure that environmental buffs and researchers will both find this book to be an invaluable resource.

Dayle Barry
Former Coordinator
Conservation Data Center

It is a singular pleasure for me to commend the writers of this Field Guide to the Plant and Marine Communities of the Virgin Islands. *Not only does this document identify and describe plant life and animal life, but it climbs the highest peaks and explores the depths of marine life, so that this book will, indeed, be of "great importance to residents, researchers and visitors."*

This is the kind of work that the Cooperative Extension Service of the University of the Virgin Islands takes pride in presenting with other partners. This is the result of the collaboration that is so essential to our existence. We must thank the Virgin Islands Department of Planning and Natural Resources, the Virgin Islands Department of Agriculture, the USDA Natural Resources Conservation Service, the National Park Service, the U.S. Geological Survey, the Nature Conservancy, the Island Resources Foundation, the National Oceanic and Atmospheric Administration, and the local scientists and technical experts who contributed to this work. In addition, we must thank The Eastern Caribbean Center and the Conservation Data Center.

As readers and researchers explore this field guide, they will learn of the Virgin Islands' past and present, and they will be enlightened into preserving it for the future. With the intensity of natural disasters, we must look at other phenomena besides hurricanes and earthquakes. Volcanic eruptions and the most recent tsunami in Southeast Asia and Africa have also given us cause to be concerned and to learn more about our natural environment. They have alerted us to the possibility of environmental changes that can occur without much warning. This Field Guide to the Plant and Marine Communities of the Virgin Islands *will equip us with relevant data about our plant and marine communities so that, as we expand, we will construct creatively, with great consideration given to our unique communities.*

I hope that this field guide will achieve its intended purposes.

Mr. Kwame Garcia, Director
Cooperative Extension Service
University of the Virgin Islands

Published by The University of the Virgin Islands
International Standard Book Number (ISBN) 0-615-12992-7

Author's Note:
A publication of this scope contains numerous facts and opinions. Any mistakes and in accuracies are the sole responsibility of the authors. Maps are not intended for navigational purposes.
T. Thomas
B. Devine

Detailed maps of the terrestrial vegetation and marine communities of St. Croix, St. John, St. Thomas, and Water Island were completed in 2001 by:

The Eastern Caribbean Center, Conservation Data Center, at the University of the Virgin Islands
and
University of the Virgin Islands
Cooperative Extension Service

Working in conjunction with:
Virgin Islands Department of Planning and Natural Resources; Virgin Islands Department of Agriculture; USDA Natural Resources Conservation Service; National Park Service; U.S. Geological Survey; Nature Conservancy; Island Resources Foundation; National Oceanic and Atmospheric Administration; Local Scientists and Technical Experts

This publication was partially funded by a grant from the
Virgin Islands Department of Agriculture Urban and Community Forestry Assistance Program

Table of Contents

Foreword

From "peak to reef," from the summits of our highest places to the ocean shelf, the native vegetation and marine habitats of the Virgin Islands are of great importance to residents, researchers, and visitors. Few publications adequately describe these local plant and marine community types, their classification, and their distribution throughout the Territory.

This field guide, produced cooperatively by several organizations and many individuals, is meant to educate people, act as a field reference, and showcase the unique and valuable natural areas in the Virgin Islands. It is also meant to teach about the critical link between the land and the sea, with an emphasis on how human beings impact it and their responsibility for these natural resources as stewards of the planet.

Acknowledgements

Contributing Authors: Caroline Rogers, Ph.D., Rafe Boulon, Eleanor Gibney, Gary Ray, Ph.D., Rudy O'Reilly, Roy Watlington, Julie Wright, David Brewer, Jeff Miller, Carolyn Stengel, Douglas McNair, Pedro Nieves

Technical Director: Clarice Clarke

Technical Consultant: Eva M. Maddox

Contributors: Laverne Ragster, Ph.D., Carol Mayes, Jean Pierre Bacle, Kevel Lindsey, Edward Towle, Ph.D., Christy Loomis, Dayle Barry, Stevie Henry, Nicolas Drayton, Marcia Taylor, Richard Nemeth, Ph.D., Joan Farrelly, Virginia Garrison, James Beets, Don Catanzaro, Ph.D., Lance Lewand, Barbara Kojis, Ph.D., Evonne Zullo, Paige Rothenberger, James Battey, Ph.D., Mayra Suarez, Olasee Davis

Photography: Toni Thomas, Barry Devine, Ph.D., Dale Morton, Christy Loomis, Matt Kendall, Curtis Kruer, Carol Kramer-Burke, Cheryl Pawlowski, Caroline Rogers, Ph.D., Rafe Boulon, Gary Ray, Ph.D., Roy Watlington, Jeff Miller, Dana Ulsamer

Graphic Design: Karin Donaldson

Editors: Eva M. Maddox, Valerie Combie, Ph.D., Diane Devine

Landscapes and Seascapes: Link of Life

"Life reaches its greatest diversity in tropical seas and tropical forests. There I first began to realize the essential similarities in plan and function among all the diverse living landscapes and seascapes of our planetary surface—the essential unity of the living world."

Marston Bates
The Forest and the Sea, 1960

Few places in the world show the vital connection between the land and the sea as clearly as within small tropical island ecosystems. An important physical, chemical, and biological web connects these natural worlds, from the summit to the submerged continental shelf, linking priceless resources, people, and their activities.

For millions of years, the landscape of the Virgin Islands has been eroding, changing, and evolving naturally. Weathering and stormwater runoff erode these materials by natural drainage guts to the coastal wetlands and the sea beyond. Plants and their root systems filter and slow the passage of stormwater as it drains over and through the landscape to the sea. Near-shore coral, seagrass, algal, and fish communities grow on a steady input of beneficial materials and nutrients from the land.

Annaly Gut, St. Croix

Over long geological periods, interdependence between the land and sea has developed. These connections are shown most clearly in the dynamic places where freshwater streams and salt ponds meet. This coastal fringe, neither land nor sea, composed of mangrove forests, wetlands, and cobble beaches, nurturing billions of creatures, including microscopic organisms, along the shore line and in the deeper marine environments.

In the last several hundred years and, more importantly, within the past 25 years, the human impact of poor land-use practices has become a significant influence in this land-sea relationship. Bare soils, cleared of their protective natural vegetative cover, expose coastal habitats and marine communities to the damaging effects of unfiltered stormwater runoff that contains eroded sediment, nutrients, and biological pathogens. Where steep hillsides and lush valleys drained clear water in the past, now dirt roads are chocolate brown with runoff, solid waste, sediment, sewage, and microscopic organisms.

A beautiful and intriguing world surrounds us. As a result of human activities, however, negative impacts, both subtle and obvious, are having a tremendous effect on this fragile world. Frequent plumes of brown stormwater now flood the once-pristine coastal waters of the islands. Through a heightened understanding of our natural island environment, better planning, and more strategic actions, we can reverse these negative changes. This publication is a small step toward that goal.

General Description of the Virgin Islands

The U.S. Virgin Islands (USVI) are located in the eastern extreme of the Greater Antilles at approximately 18° 20'N latitude, 64° 50'W longitude. They are comprised of four main islands: St. Croix, St. Thomas, Water Island, and St. John. Surrounded by more than 90 islands, cays, and rocks, the USVI are among the most biologically interesting areas of the world. St. Thomas and St. John are of volcanic origin, rising from a geological shelf that includes the British Virgin Islands and Puerto Rico. The shelf is surrounded by deep water. St. Croix, commonly called a "sea mount," is sedimentary and carbonate in origin. It sits on a smaller shelf, separated from St. Thomas and St. John by the Virgin Islands trough, which is 4,685 meters (15,370 feet) deep and 64 kilometers (40 miles) wide.

St. Croix, the southern and eastern-most of the Virgin Islands, is the largest and most agricultural island, with a total area

of 53,480 acres (85 square miles). Following an east-west axis, it is about 34 kilometers (21 miles) long and 9.6 kilometers (6 miles) at the widest point. The maximum elevation occurs at Mr. Eagle (332 meters 1,088 feet). Eastern and western ranges in the northern part of St. Croix graduate to a broad and rolling expanse of coastal plain in the south. The narrow shelf surrounding the island descends gradually, allowing for growth of a long fringing reef around much of the coastline.

St. Thomas, the most westerly island and the second largest, is less than half St. Croix's size, with a total area of

about 19,000 acres (32 square miles). It measures about 19 kilometers long (12 miles) by 5 kilometers (3 miles) wide. With the highest peak in the islands,

St. Thomas is topped at 474 meters (1556 feet) at Crown Mountain, where remnants of native upland moist forest can be found. St. Thomas's predominantly steep topography limits reef growth to shallower locations along the irregular coastline. Volcanic mountains with steep slopes dominate the landscape, and coastal plains are few in number. The island, the main tourism center for cruise ships and resort hotels in the USVI, suffers from dense urban over-development.

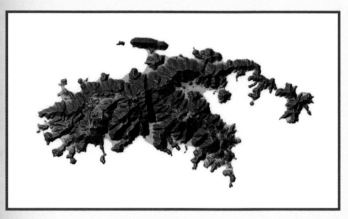

St. John, two miles to the east of St. Thomas, is roughly 13 kilometers (8 miles) long by 4 kilometers (2.5 miles) wide, with a land area of only 12,000 acres (19 square miles). Bordeaux Mountain is the highest elevation at 392 meters (1,277 feet). Like St. Thomas, steeply sloped volcanic mountains dominate the topography, and numerous bays are found along the irregular shoreline. Pockets of upland moist forest grow on the island's mountain peaks, sand beaches abound, and the pace of life seems slower than on St. Thomas. The Virgin Islands National Park and Biosphere Reserve encompasses 56% of the land area of St. John. Park waters surround the island, attracting more than one million visitors a year.

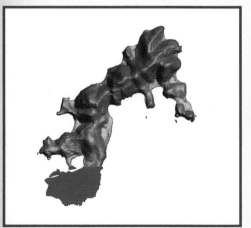

Water Island, at 492 acres, is the largest cay in the Virgin Islands and the smallest of the four main islands that make up the USVI. Indeed, the U.S. Department of the Interior only recently transferred Water Island to the USVI government (see next page). It is located about half a mile south-southwest of St. Thomas's main harbor, Charlotte Amalie. Water Island is about 4 kilometers (2.5 miles) long by about 1.5 kilometers (1 mile) wide. The maximum elevation on this dry and rocky island is 984 meters (300 feet) above sea level. Despite its small size, the island has a rich natural diversity, with an irregular coastline that creates many bays, wetlands, ponds, and coral reefs.

Water Island or "Isla de Agua," Receives Official Status as the Newest U.S Virgin Island

In 1996, Water Island officially became the smallest of the four main U.S. Virgin Islands when it passed from the control of the U.S. Government to the territorial Government of the Virgin Islands. Located south of the Charlotte Amalie harbor, Water Island, at 492 acres (198 hectares), is also considered to be the largest of the cays surrounding St. Thomas.

The island's cultural history is rich. AmerIndians from the Preceramic and Ceramic period cultures, who migrated to the Virgin Islands region from coastal South America, left artifacts and other archaeological evidence of habitation in campsites around the island. Water Island's colonial history dates from the 1670s with the domination by the Danish West Indies Company for a century. The plantation Era, followed by the emancipation of slaves, brought large changes to the small island's natural terrestrial and marine resources as a result of farming, wood harvesting, livestock grazing, fishing, turtle hunting, and limestone quarrying. In 1917, the U.S. Government bought the Virgin Islands, including Water Island, from Denmark. Water Island was used strategically during WWII. After the war, the U.S. Government eventually sold some of its property to residents and transferred the rest to the Territory of the Virgin Islands in 1996.

Although Water Island's natural resources have been degraded by human impacts, a variety of terrestrial and coastal environments still exist there. Most of the island's plant communities are predominantly dry and not as varied as those found on the larger Virgin Islands. Dry forests, shrublands, and former pasturelands are most common. Sandy and rocky beaches, salt ponds, and mangrove wetlands are found along the intricately winding coastline. The coast is rugged with areas of sparse vegetation on bedrock. Water Island, also known as Isla de Agua, reportedly was named for the freshwater ponds that once existed on the island. Any existing fresh, salt, and brackish ponds are too small to have been detected in aerial photographs used to create the Rapid Ecological Assessment

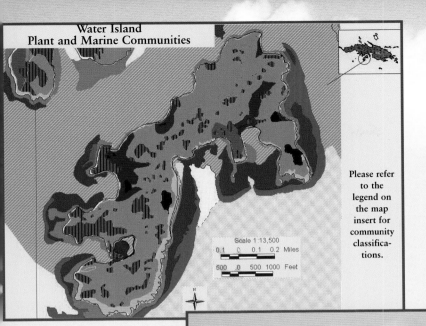

Water Island Plant and Marine Communities

Please refer to the legend on the map insert for community classifications.

Scale 1:13,500

0.1 0 0.1 0.2 Miles

500 0 500 1000 Feet

Coastal hedge and thicket/scrub shrublands commonly grow on Water Island's coastal bedrock.

(REA) GIS maps featured in this publication. Offshore marine communities are rich and diverse. Extensive coral reefs, colonized pavement, and coral-covered bedrock are common in the waters surrounding the island. Seagrass beds are found in many bays, and protected areas and offshore currents supply the clean waters surrounding the island.

Hassel Island in foreground and Water Island in background.

Climate

The Virgin Islands are classified as subtropical, cooler than the nearby tropical mainland of Central America, because of the cooling effects of the surrounding waters. The islands are low in elevation and have little rainfall when compared with larger Caribbean islands to the west. Although average rainfall is about 140 centimeters (55 inches), it varies widely from island to island and across each island. The average temperature is 26° C (79° F). A number of animal and plant populations fluctuate seasonally throughout the islands depending on rainfall pattern, elevation, and aspect.

Stormwater is often forced to cascade over hillsides and roads because man has degraded the natural drainage systems such as pervious soil surfaces, guts and streams.

Winds and Waves

The tradewinds (Easterlies) blow consistently from the east. Major seasonal variations are a result of the northerly Bermuda High and the southerly Equatorial Trough. From December through February, winds intensify from 11 to 21 knots sixty percent of the time. These "Christmas Winds" blow very strongly from the north but are reduced in velocity from March through May. In summer, winds increase in strength once again, becoming the lightest from September through November, except during storm events.

The average tidal range in the islands is less than 1 foot, and tidal currents are generally weak. Waves come from the east and north in winter and the southeast in summer. They are typically 1 to 3 feet high during calm weather and can reach 10 to 12 feet in winter. The swells from the north create strong, long-shore currents that concentrate wave energy on exposed headlands and beaches. This influences not only the marine communities found in this area but also the coastal vegetation.

Geological History of the Virgin Islands

By Roy A. Watlington

Columnar-jointed keratophyres of the Water Island Formation are shown in the inset (lower left) and in a view of the cliff face near the St. Thomas airport where distinct geometric lines reveal the original lava flows.

All of the Virgin Islands began forming millions of years ago from volcanic eruptions on the ocean floor under several miles of water. At that time, the Caribbean Basin and Central America did not exist as we know them. The presently existing islands of the Caribbean Sea had not yet been formed. Constant motion of the Earth's crust led to the continual creation of volcanoes and caused vertical motion of the seafloor. Melted volcanic material, known as magma, flowed from volcanic vents as lava, ash, and pyroclastic flows. These cooled to form the oldest igneous rocks in the Virgin Islands, exemplified today by the Water Island Formation. The oldest of these rocks, found near the Cyril E. King Airport on St. Thomas, was found by means of radioisotope dating to be approximately 108 million years old.

Hydrothermally altered rocks in the Water Island Formation located on the East End of St. John.

The names of formations arise from the locations where the collections were first charted by geologists. For example, the oldest volcanic rocks in the northern Virgin Islands were first identified on Water Island by geologist Thomas W. Donnelly. They comprise Water Island and most of the southern coasts of

Geological Research In the USVI

Dr. Thomas Donnelly, 1999.

The most comprehensive project undertaken to understand the geology of the Virgin Islands started back in the late 1950s when Professor H. Hess brought his graduate students to the region. John T. Whetten specialized on St. Croix; Charles E. Helsley focused on the British Virgin Islands, and Thomas W. Donnelly (left) concentrated on St. Thomas and St. John. More recent studies by Denis K. Hubbard, Douglas Rankin, and others have expanded this body of knowledge.

St. John and St. Thomas. During the same period, magma also cooled within established rock to form some of the rocks identified as intrusive by Donnelly on St. Thomas and by Douglas Rankin on St. John. Listed from older to younger, the other formations recognized today are the Careen Hill Intrusives, distinguished recently by geologist Douglas Rankin, and the Louisenhoj Formation. Next followed formations that include rocks with origins in the remains of ancient corals: the Outer Brass Limestone and the Tutu Formation, with Mandahl, Picara Point, and Congo Cay rocks classified under the latter.

In a class of their own are plutonic rocks, like those in the Virgin Gorda Baths, which resulted when magma penetrated into rock without being exposed to the air until many years after cooling and hardening. Some have been dated to be approximately 24 million years old. The youngest of the igneous rocks, they are also found in several other isolated locations in the USVI. John Whetten was the first to describe the geology of St. Croix in the context of tectonic plate motion. The work for his dissertation led to the basis for understanding how St. Croix was formed. Although his work was later supplemented by the work of Denis Hubbard and others, Whetten identified and named most of the rock formations recognized there today. He observed similarities between the rocks of St. Croix's Caledonia Formation and the rocks of the Water Island Formation of the northern USVI. These are among the oldest rock assemblages on the respective islands.

Tilted Louisenhoj Formation beds in Bordeaux Bay, St. Thomas.

The Louisenhoj Formation includes the hard blue-gray rocks known locally as blue beach. Blue beach cobbles (above) are weathered out of a solid rock surface.

The mollusk shells above were fossilized in rocks of the Tutu Formation while dinosaurs still walked the earth.

Rocks of St. Croix's Caledonia Formation pictured here are among the oldest rock assemblages in the Virgin Islands. They are similar to Water Island Formation rocks found in the northern U.S. Virgin Islands.

Local variation in the general motion of the Caribbean tectonic plate may have caused the widening of the Virgin Islands Basin, gradually separating St. Croix from Puerto Rico and the northern islands. At one point, St. Croix may have consisted of two separate mountain ranges on the seafloor, which were later uplifted and exposed. Corals that had grown to great thicknesses in the submerged valley between the ranges solidified to build up the lowland and give St. Croix its present form. An abundance of "caliche" soil in central St. Croix and the ancient reefs dramatically exposed by road cuts provide evidence of this submarine period in St. Croix's geological history.

Rocks in the formations of the Virgin Islands region may include igneous, sedimentary, and metamorphic rocks. Sedimentary rocks are still being formed by corals and by the cementing of shallow marine sediments.

None of today's hills in the Virgin Islands are—or ever were—volcanic cones. Instead, our hills were formed by folding, uplift, and weathering. Volcanism no longer occurs in the Virgin Islands or in any of the islands of the Greater Antilles. The only volcanoes to erupt significantly in the eastern Caribbean since the Africans and Europeans came to the region in the 15th century have been on Martinique, Guadeloupe, St. Vincent, and Montserrat as well as in the ocean north of Grenada. Montserrat's Soufriére Hills volcano and the submarine volcano near Grenada named Kick'em Jenny continue to erupt in the 21st century.

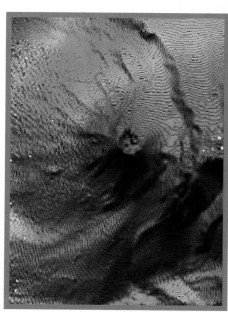

Kick'em Jenny, a submarine volcano near Grenada, revealed from above by a NOAA multi-beam survey, erupted in December 2001.

Cultural History of the Virgin Islands:
A Short Primer
By David M. Brewer

Original Migrations into the Caribbean

The earliest evidence of migration into the Caribbean appears to date from approximately 4000 B.C. These initial visitors generally lived along the coast and had a lithic (stone-working) and shell technology. They probably were intricate weavers, and they may have used wooden tools or gourds as well. They had not developed ceramic technology, so their sites do not contain numerous shards, or ceramic vessel fragments, as so many other later sites will, although piles of shell remains, or middens, are usually quite evident. These Preceramic peoples are also referred to as Archaic people, and what little we know of them is based on the archaeological remains of their food processing. Almost nothing is known of their style of dress, the houses or villages in which they lived, or their languages and social systems.

Although archaeologists are not in agreement regarding the avenue by which these people came into the Caribbean islands, the earliest known sites in Cuba and Puerto Rico seem to indicate a Central American or Yucatan crossing. They do acknowledge, however, that other Preceramic populations eventually made their way up from South America, and these migrations would continue over the centuries. "In the Virgin Islands the earliest dates for their sites are 1000–2000 B.C., with the latest dates approximately AD 200" (Lundberg 1997:5). When Columbus arrived, a small isolated group of Preceramic people were reported to be still living in western Cuba. They practiced horticulture (i.e., they gathered wild and semi-domesticated plants such as cassava, yucca, and yams), but they did not plant extensive domesticated crops. Therefore,

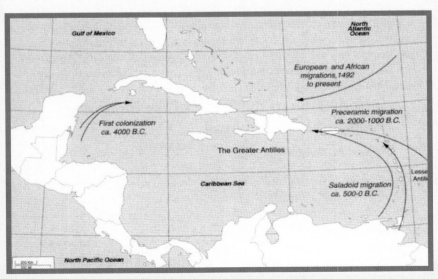

Early migration routes into the Caribbean.

these earliest people were probably seminomadic, moving from place to place as resources dwindled or seasons changed, and probably living in small familial groups. In general, the overall population throughout the Caribbean during the initial migrations, and for at least 2,000 years afterward, was very limited.

The earliest visitors to the Caribbean, then, are thought to have begun their migration into the Greater Antilles (Cuba, Jamaica, Hispaniola, and Puerto Rico) by as early as 4000 B.C. This first migration probably occurred by way of the Yucatan and Central America. They explored the lands and waters, enjoyed the bounty of the forests and the sea, and raised their families for over 2,000 years before we began to see evidence of their lifestyle in just a few brief glimpses through the window of time. One of these is the Krum Bay Archeological Site on St. Thomas.

Archaeologists today generally accept that a second migration of Preceramic people occurred out of the Orinoco basin from South America between 2000 and 1000 B.C., and we should keep in mind that this movement between the islands was probably continuous. A number of stone tools, including celts, hand axes, hammer stones, and chipped, pecked, and ground stone blades were recovered among the shell debris at Krum Bay. Among the food shell remains were Ark shells, clam, conch, and crab, as well as fish and turtle bones. Thus, the people who lived here, however briefly, must have gained most of their sustenance from the sea and processed their foods using stone tools. Evidence of fire-heated rocks seems to indicate that they cooked these foods on open fires.

Little else is known about these earliest of inhabitants to the islands, and Preceramic sites are extremely rare. Radiocarbon dates for the Krum Bay site show that it was occupied during the period 225–450 B.C., or 2,200 to 2,500 years ago. It is suggested that these early prehistoric adventurers probably made their way up the Lesser Antilles from Venezuela, because a number of the stone tools resemble those found in Aruba and Curacao, as well as in the recognized Preceramic "Ortoiroid" culture of Trinidad, named after the archaeological site of Otoire located there, which has been dated to approximately B.C. 800.

Early Classic Ceramic "Saladoid" Period
People who made ceramics and grew food crops began to move into the Lesser Antilles between 500 and 250 B.C. Archaeologists generally agree that these people must have come from South America because the beautiful white-and-red painted pottery, adorned with zone-incised cross-hatching, is similar to that found at the Venezuelan site of Saladero (hence "Saladoid"). The Saladoid, the ancestors of the Taino, had a rich and prosperous life among the islands, especially on the larger islands of the Greater Antilles, which allowed for large agricultural farms and villages.

Classic saladoid-style bowl.

An earlier migration of these people probably began about 500–300 B.C., and so many land crab shells were associated with these early ceramic-making farmers that they were once regarded as the "Crab People." Later, archaeologists realized that between farming (especially that of cassava, yams, plantains, papaya, and cotton), hunting and fishing, and possibly raising small tree rodents ("hutia"), dogs, and iguanas for food, these early Taino were able to develop into large groups, which in turn splintered off and became villages throughout the Antilles. They developed a strong spiritual and religious system of beliefs and rituals that were probably influential in determining various social structures, enforcing cultural styles and taboos, and guiding the timing of annual festive events.

Culture Change: The Ostionoid and the Classic Taino Period

Beginning in approximately A.D. 600, changes started taking place that indicated a series of major cultural shifts, especially in ceramic styles. The distinctive Saladoid pottery, so finely made and with its elaborate white-and-red painting, was replaced by thicker, less decorated, more utilitarian wares. Large-scale agriculture and the use of terraced farming also became evident. The presence of ball courts and ball-game paraphernalia can also be seen. This was also accompanied by an extensive trade in items (and ideas) from across the Caribbean and the Yucatan, as well as up and down the Lesser Antilles and present-day Venezuela. Evidence exists that the earlier "Archaic" Preceramic peoples were incorporated into the larger sphere of influence generated by the more successful society of the ceramic agriculturalists' during this period.

Although the interaction of these various groups was probably marked by economic and political rivalry, they began to coalesce culturally into what has become known as the Classic Taino. Sometimes referred to as "Arawak" or Arawakan, the Taino may be considered a distinct people of the circum-Caribbean basin who simply shared aspects of the Arawakan-based language, still spoken by the elderly in Guyana and Suriname. This lends some credence to the origins of the Taino out of South America. The Lucayan Taino were the first people encountered by Columbus. By that time (1492), the Taino-occupied islands had already been invaded by another South American tribe that had worked its way up the Lesser Antilles slowly over the preceding 500 years or so. Less prone to peaceful coexistence and more to political rivalry, these new people—the Island Caribs—prided themselves on their masculine warrior lifestyle.

Island Caribs, or Kalinago

By the time of the arrival of the Europeans, the Island Caribs (as distinguished from the Carib tribes of the South American mainland), also known as the Kalinago, had worked their way up the Lesser Antilles to the point that they had probably reached as far as present-day St. Croix. In fact, St. Croix may have been occupied by both Carib and Taino at the time of Columbus's second voyage in 1493. The Island Caribs were considered dangerous by early explorers, based on their fierce nature and their skill with poisoned arrows. The entry in Columbus's journal for 26 November 1492 stated: "All the people that he has found up to today, he says, are very frightened of those of *can iba or can ima*," which was Hispanicized to *car iba*. It was from this that the people, and later the place, came to be known as Carib and later Caribbean. Later French missionaries who lived with the Island Caribs recorded their stories of having come from the South American continent. In fact, Carib communities are still living there today, as well as on Dominica, Guadeloupe, and Martinique.

European Encounter and Its Aftermath

At the time of the European "discovery" of the West Indies, the islands of the Greater and Lesser Antilles were well populated and had already undergone various migrations and culture shifts for over 3,000 years. The cultures of the

Caribbean, however, were doomed. Because of slavery, acculturation, disease, forced removal, and finally genocide, the islands were depopulated of the native groups within a hundred years. The indigenous Indian populations were exterminated by the Europeans in their plans to conquer and extract available natural resources. Today, only remnants of the cultures of the great adventurous people who settled these islands remain.

The population found throughout the islands today is a diverse blend of people who have migrated here over the past 500 years. Many Africans and people from other parts of the world were captured, enslaved, and brought forcibly to the islands. At different times, the countries of Denmark, Spain, England, Netherlands, France, and the Knights of Malta had an interest here. The Plantation Era lasted for centuries with the growth of sugar cane and manufacture of molasses, rum, indigo and other products for the triangle trade. In 1917, the U.S. purchased the Virgin Islands from Denmark, and they became a Territory of the United States.

Conceptualized drawing of a classic Taino village.

Natural and Human Influences
that Affect Plant and Marine Communities

Environmental change in the West Indies in the recent past has been dramatic. Whereas a warm and moist climate prevails today, cooler climates existed before this period, approximately 15,000–20,000 years ago, and other ecosystem types adapted to this regime. Several natural processes—earthquakes, fires, landslides, and hurricanes—are critical in shaping the environments of the islands and their animal, plant, and marine communities.

Coral Bay rainstorm.

Hurricanes, Tropical Waves and Storms

Hurricanes, tropical waves, and storms are common from August to November when several inches of rain can fall quickly, creating massive runoff into wetlands, bays, and coastal areas. Over the past 25 years, eight major hurricanes have caused extensive damage to vegetation communities and coral reefs throughout the Virgin Islands. Recovery of coral reefs and forests from these natural disturbances takes from decades to centuries and is hindered by a variety of human impacts, such as overfishing, ship groundings, anchor damage, land clearing, sedimentation, and non-point source pollution.

Storm- and wind-damaged vegetation.

Natural stresses, like tropical storms and hurricanes, cause some of the greatest and most extensive damage to coastal wetlands and coral reefs, already weakened by other stresses. Coral diseases and coral bleaching during periods of high sea-surface temperatures, although considered natural phenomenon, may be linked more closely with human activities than previously thought.

Human Influences

The Virgin Islands were never connected to a continental land mass. They acquired their flora and fauna by invasion of continental species. Originally, these islands were almost completely forested, but European settlers cleared a large percentage of the forests during the Plantation Era, which lasted from the 1600s through the 1800s. No definitive descriptions of the original forests have ever been discovered, and current descriptions are only approximate. Botanists think that much of the islands were originally covered with dense, closed-canopy forests and small, perennial, freshwater streams flowed down the hillsides in some locations.

The islands' early inhabitants, Pre-Columbian Indians, introduced some plants and animals, but they probably had little major impact on the forests. Colonization of the islands by European settlers caused extensive destruction of the native vegetation and dramatically altered the natural landscape. During the Colonial Era, the dense forest cover was cut to harvest timber and clear land for cultivation, plantation development, and other agricultural activities. Valuable tree species were removed, and forest canopies were opened. Sun-exposed soils dried and eroded, and weedy plants often aggressively colonized the clearings. Settlers also introduced many non-native plants and foraging animals that further threatened the existence of unique native plant species.

The destruction of original natural vegetation or virgin forests was extensive throughout the Virgin Islands. At the end of the Plantation Era, the downturn in sugar production in the 1800s and the emancipation of the slaves in 1848 resulted in less intensive agricultural land use and limited recovery of the native forests. Land use changed to small-scale intensive farming and grazing. With this change, the natural vegetation began to recover some of its former structure. In the last several decades, however, soil erosion and runoff caused by high rainfall and steep slopes, combined with road construction, land clearing, agriculture, alteration of natural drainage ways, and the filling of coastal areas, have had a tremendous impact on the lowland coastal wetlands and near-shore marine communities. Furthermore, population growth, tourism, and expanded urban and residential development in the 20th century once again dramatically increased land-clearing activities that impact native plant communities.

Mangrove roots stabilize the shoreline.

Habitat loss and disturbance are threatening the high biological diversity—the richness and abundance—of living species found in the islands. In addition, the introduction of non-native plants and animals has selectively altered plant and wildlife composition and slowed or stopped natural recovery. With respect to marine ecosystems, sedimentation from runoff and dredging activities is probably the most detrimental local influence on coral reefs, a problem common to many Caribbean islands. Sediments can smother coral organisms and reduce light levels below needed requirements. In some cases, terrestrial pathogens have even been found to cause disease in sea fans and perhaps stony corals. More than 30 coral diseases and syndromes have now been recognized, and only four or five have known pathogens. In addition, recreational uses, boating, anchor damage, and pollution from solid and liquid wastes have a deleterious, long-term impact.

The climate, soils, topography, and location of the Virgin Islands contribute to variation in the natural vegetation. The natural conditions affecting plants and plant community development are:

Subtropical climate - Virgin Islands' natural vegetation is classified as subtropical because the islands are in a tropical region with seasonal variation marked by dry/wet seasons rather than by cold/hot temperatures. The warm and generally dry climate varies slightly, less than a 10° difference between the coolest and warmest air temperatures.

Wind - Easterly tradewinds are almost constant, producing communities of wind-adapted plants in exposed areas at low elevations on the islands' eastern windward sides. Wind may also play a major part in the spreading of pollen as evidenced by a predominance of small, non-showy flowers on native plants that are probably wind-pollinated.

Rainfall - Average rainfall can vary considerably from month to month and year to year. Annual wet and dry seasons are typical. This variability affects plant community distribution.

Hurricanes - Recurrent hurricanes damage forests, create gaps in the canopy that expose forests to future stress, and also disrupt progression towards a climax or mature forest stage. Hurricanes also alter forest composition with some tree species seeming to be more susceptible to destructive hurricane forces.

Location and topography - Island topography is characterized by central mountain ranges and mostly small coastal plains. Mountainous terrain with steep slopes is common; indeed, 50% of the land exceeds slopes of 25% to 35%. Depending on location, plants must adapt to rapid stormwater runoff from steep slopes, which results in soil moisture deficits on hillsides and flooding in lowland areas. The microclimate at higher elevations is often moister and cooler than that of lowland areas, which also affects plant community development.

Soils - Most soils in the Virgin Islands formed from basic volcanic rocks. Soils derived from limestone rocks also formed on St. Croix, with small pockets on St. Thomas and St. John. Soils are generally neutral to alkaline, fine textured, clay or clay-loams. Different vegetative types are supported by various soil types and conditions.

Aspect (slope direction) - Greater wind and sun exposure on south- and east-facing slopes create drier conditions. Reduced exposure and more rainfall on north- and west-facing slopes result in moister conditions and moister plant communities.

Coastal exposure - Coastal zones exposed to more salt spray, salt blast, and storm intensity limit plant growth to only salt- and wind-tolerant species.

Human activities have dramatically affected plant communities in the Virgin Islands. Deforestation, land clearing, agriculture, the introduction of non-native plants, and residental and urban developments have left only remnants of the original plant associations.

A Brief History of Vegetation Classification in the Caribbean

The islands of the West Indies form a chain of more than 1,000 islands stretching almost 4,800 kilometers from the Bahamas to Curacao. Although many well-known botanists have visited the islands within the past several hundred years, collecting plants and interpreting the vegetation systems they found, no comprehensive flora exists for the whole region. Over these years, various systems of vegetation classification have been proposed, used, and replaced.

The Virgin Islands were among the first Caribbean Islands to be explored and described by botanists. West (1793), Schlectendal (1828), Krebs (1847), von Eggers (1879), Millspaugh (1902), Urban (1902), Borgeson (1923), Britton (1918), Britton and Wilson (1923-1926), Beard (1945), Little and Wadsworth (1964), Little, Wadsworth and Woodbury (1974), Liogier (1965), Acevedo-Rodriguez and Woodbury (1985), Liogier and Martorell (1982), Woodbury and Weaver (1987), Proctor (1989), and Acevedo-Rodriguez (1996) all spent a significant amount of time describing the existing flora and developing vegetation classifications. Beard (1944, 1955) contributed the most important regional system, which is based on plant composition, plant architecture, and habitat; it is still in use today.

This field guide follows a vegetation classification system prepared specifically for the Virgin Islands based on past regional classification systems by Beard, Woodbury, and Weaver, merged and cross-referenced with newer systems: the Federal Geographic Data

Committee (FGDC), the National Vegetation Classification System (NVCS), and the Caribbean Vegetation Types. These newer classification systems are attempts to standardize national and global protocol for classifying, describing, and/or mapping vegetative cover.

The classification of plant communities and vegetation is an inexact science, useful in interpreting similarities and differences, but prone to problems that arise from trying to standardize subtle variations in composition and structure. Classification of plant communities is also complex because of the blending of types across environmental gradients, leading to changes in species composition, abundance, and morphology. Past land-use activities and fluctuation in the natural environment contribute to this complexity.

Gifted Field Botanist

For 70 years Professor Roy Orlo Woodbury trained botanists and students in Florida, Puerto Rico, and the Virgin Islands, generously sharing his expansive knowledge of Caribbean flora and natural history.

Professor Woodbury studied botany at the University of Miami and eventually taught there for 21 years. Known as an excellent and charismatic teacher, he attracted many students, even nonscience majors, and impressed many with his conservation ethics. After Miami, Professor Woodbury began a career at the Agricultural Experiment Station at the University of Puerto Rico, where he remained for 33 years, focusing on plant taxonomy, field research, and teaching. He was an explorer at heart; as such, he rediscovered many plant species previously considered extinct in Puerto Rico. Seven plants were named after him; most are very rare. One, *Machaonia woodburyana* (featured in the section on Shrublands), is known only from populations found on St. John and on Virgin Gorda.

During his very productive life, Woodbury completed a checklist of the flora of St. John, developed one of the first vegetation maps of St. John, and completed *A Vegetation Survey of St. John and Hassel Island.* In addition, he organized and participated in many other projects and studies. He coauthored *Common Trees and Shrubs of Puerto Rico and the Virgin Islands, Volume Two,* and also *A Flora of Buck Island Reef National Monument.*

Upon retirement, Woodbury continued to share his knowledge with students and plant enthusiasts, and he served as a consultant to many organizations, including the Smithsonian Institution. In 1984, he was awarded the title of Professor Emeritus from the University of Puerto Rico. Professor Woodbury is remembered by many local botanists and other scientists for his fine sense of humor and his extensive research throughout the Caribbean region.

Professor Roy Woodbury

A UVI reference collection featuring **Malpighia woodburyana** *and* **Machaonia woodburyana** *discovered by Roy Woodbury.*

of the Virgin Islands

The moist forests of the Virgin Islands are vegetation communities defined as *forests* because tree crowns interlock to form closed canopies. Moist forests are the tallest forests in the islands wherein some tree species may grow to almost 100 feet (over 30 meters high). About 75% of the trees are broad-leaved and evergreen. The rest of the trees are deciduous, typically shedding all or most of their leaves during the dry season. The tallest types of moist forest formations generally have three forest layers, known as canopy strata, whereas the shorter types have only two layers.

An uncommon moist forest shrub,
Gonzalagunia spicata.

Moist forests are divided into different zones based primarily on elevation and moisture availability. Many of the same plant species grow throughout these zones and are adapted for a wide range of conditions. These zones include the following:

Hog turd (Andira inermis), *a common moist forest tree.*

- *Upland evergreen moist forest*—On protected upland mountain summits and ridges.
- *Gallery moist forest*—In riparian (stream side) areas associated with natural drainage guts (intermittent stream channels) that carry runoff from upper elevations.
- *Basin moist forest*—In protected coastal flat areas behind beaches where rainwater drains and collects from hillsides.

Moist Forest Cover in the U.S.V.I.

St. John (10.43%)

St. Thomas (2.95%)

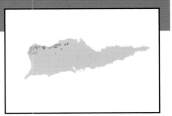

St. Croix (1.28%)

Upland moist forest found on Crown Mountain, St. Thomas.

STRATEGIES FOR SURVIVAL: *How Moist Forest Plants Adapt to Wetter Conditions and Compete for Sunlight*

Plant adaptations and unique life forms found in tropical rainforests can also be found in the moist forests of the Virgin Islands.

Motherbush (Lepianthes peltatum)

Miconia laevigata *shrub*

Buttress roots

Broad-leaf evergreen trees are also dominant in tropical rainforests of the Amazon region, central Africa, and eastern Puerto Rico. Broad-leaf evergreen trees thrive in environments with enough moisture to allow them to continue photosynthesis throughout the year. As they usually have no need to save energy and moisture use by dropping leaves during the driest parts of the year, they remain "evergreen" throughout the year. Broad, flat, and thin leaves are best for capturing light, and leaf size increases with precipitation levels. Leaves may also be leathery and thick to withstand sunlight exposure in the forest upper canopy or during periodic dry periods.

Drip tips are long-pointed tips at ends of leaves that channel off excessive moisture to prevent fungus growth and loss of efficiency during photosynthesis. Like many trees in the tropical rainforest, drip tips can be found on the leaves of a number of moist forest plant species in the Virgin Islands.

Buttress or plank tree roots are widespreading roots that form at trunk bases to support several of the moist forest's tallest trees. Tall trees can develop extensive shallow root systems in the nutrient poor soils of the tropical rainforests or in the clayey, unstable, or rocky soils found in the moist forest zones of the Virgin Islands.

Epiphytes are nonparasitic plants that grow on other plants and sometimes on rocks. They do not extract nutrients directly from the host plant, but they can

Epiphytic native orchids and anthuriums

affect the host by taking up space and light. About 30%–60% of the plants in the dense tropical rainforests are epiphytes that grow on tree branches.

Epiphytes capture light and moisture in the upper forest canopy. Several epiphytic plants grow in the Virgin Islands, including various species of orchids, ferns, bromeliads (locally known as "air plants") and peperomia. Epiphytes have adapted to stressful conditions by developing unique and varied ways for collecting and storing limited available water and nutrient resources. These adaptations include special pores for collecting moisture from the atmosphere, leaf scales that channel water into storage, bowl-shaped reservoirs or leaf tubers that store water, succulent plant tissues, special roots that absorb nutrients from leaf litter or debris on bark, and the use of Crassulacean acid metabolism (CAM) photosynthesis to slow growth and prevent water loss.

Stranglers start as epiphytes in host trees, perhaps from a seed in a bird dropping deposited on a branch. Roots grow from the epiphyte to the ground where they thicken and merge, eventually strangling the host tree. Strangler figs found in the moist forests of the Virgin Islands include the autograph tree (*Clusia rosea*) and native ficus (*Ficus trigonata* and *F. citrifolia*).

Lianas are large woody vines that compete for sunlight by climbing to the top of the tree canopy. Ninety percent of the world's lianas are confined to the tropics, with most in rainforests where conditions are wet enough for water to be transported through long, winding stems. Two liana species that can be found in the moist forests of the Virgin Islands are prickly mampoo (*Pisonia aculeata*) and hoopvine (*Trichostigma octandrum*).

Strangler fig

The locally rare tree fern (Cyathea arborea) may only exist in St. Thomas's upland moist forest. Populations on St. John apparently died out in the mid-1990s.

Wild anthuriums (Anthurium crenatum), *known locally as rat tail or soapy soapy, grow on rocks* (center) *on Mountaintop Peak, St. Thomas.*

Location

Upland moist forests grow on mountain summits and ridges at elevations high enough to experience annual rainfall totals above 50 inches (about 1200 millimeters). This forest type is currently found only on St. Thomas and St. John. However, it probably once existed on the summits of St Croix's northwestern coastal hills, where it was degraded and replaced by drier forest types.

Community Description

About 75% of the trees are broad-leaved evergreen species. Upland moist forest includes almost all of the same plant species found in gallery and basin moist forests and many more additional species. This species diversity may occur because there are more microhabitats in upland areas and a larger range of elevations and slope steepness.

Good examples:

St. Thomas—Crown Mt. (summit and north slopes), Mountaintop (north slopes).

St. John—Bordeaux Mt. (summit and upper north slopes), Mamey Peak, and a small area at Estate Adrian.

Microclimate Diversity

Microclimate diversity is evident on the eastern and southeastern sides above 300 meters (ca. 984 feet) on Bordeaux Mt., St. John, where a remnant of a drier type of upland evergreen forest persists. This community is influenced by the prevailing direction and velocity of drying winds, slopes, and soil structure, all of which increase dry conditions. This rare forest type is characterized by a thick layer of organic duff material (decomposing leaves) at the soil surface and an abundance of rare and endangered plant species, including the federally listed and endangered St. Thomas lidflower tree (*Calyptranthes thomasiana*), as well as a rare tree in the holly family, *Ilex urbaniana*, both known only in the Virgin Islands and Puerto Rico.

Endangered St. Thomas lidflower is related to the aromatic bay rum tree.

The rare holly tree.

The fruit of the wild passionfruit vine (Passiflora laurifolia) produces a tangy juice that is a popular local drink. This vine is becoming rarer as more land is cleared.

Most trees in the upland moist forest are broad-leaf evergreen species.

Shrubs and lianas grow in the middle layer of the upland moist forest on Crown Mountain peak, St. Thomas.

Well-developed and undisturbed forests in this zone can have three main layers or strata:

Upper layer - A few taller trees more than 25 meters (82 feet) tall may emerge from a continuous closed canopy that forms at about 15 meters (49 feet) high. At present, however, trees in this zone are often less tall.

Middle layer - Shorter trees and tall shrubs are often found at about 5–10 meters (16–33 feet) growing in the shade of the taller layer.

Bottom layer - At ground level, ferns, vines, and epiphytes may be either common or absent because of low light levels at the forest floor.

Small shrubs, herbs, and ferns grow in the ground layer of the upland moist forest on the northern slopes of Mountaintop, St. Thomas.

Effects of Disturbances

Moist forest communities were taller and more diverse before they were heavily impacted by human activities. Recent severe hurricane winds (Hurricanes Hugo and Marilyn, 1989 and 1995, respectively) destroyed or damaged many of the trees in the islands' upland moist forests. Natural disturbances and land clearing have reduced the tree cover and increased sunlight exposure, which stimulates more vine, herb, small tree, and shrub growth and causes shade-loving native herbs and ferns to disappear. Native vines and large-leaved exotic vines like devil's vine (*Epipremnum aureum*) grow aggressively over shrubs and trees, competing for sunlight.

Non-native plants like the devil's vine growing in this tree and the guinea grass in the background can dominate in a moist forest that has been disturbed by human activity.

Careless Land Clearing Causes Loss of Valuable Soils and Plants

Careless land clearing (left) causes muddy storm water runoff (right).

Rare wild ginger (Alpinia sp.) is one of the native species disappearing from the cleared moist forest.

Disturbance also affects soils of moist higher altitudes that are often acidic, low in oxygen and easily degraded by exposure to sunlight. Soils on hillsides cleared of vegetation are prone to erosion.

Degraded and eroded soils can not support the diverse native flora unique to the moist forest. Many moist forest species die out and more weedy species appear, and there is also a general drying effect.

Plants grow among and on large boulders in Neltjeberg Gut, St. Thomas.

Location

Gallery moist forests grow in guts (intermittent stream channels) that drain the large upland areas (or watersheds) located in moister zones of the islands. This forest type is most common on St. John, where it fans out in all directions from the central mountains, except on the island's dry east end. On St. Thomas and St. Croix, it occurs mostly in the moister northwest. Conditions are too dry on Water Island for this forest type to develop in guts.

Good examples:

St. Croix—Caledonia Gut.

St. Thomas—Solomon or Bonne Resolution Gut.

St. John—Reef Bay Gut.

Community Description

Most tree species in this zone are ever-green, but several of the tallest trees may be deciduous, such as hog plum (*Spondias mombin*) and the native kapok or silk cotton tree (*Ceiba pentandra*). Intermittent flooding and other stressful conditions in this zone can threaten tree growth, and fewer trees survive to full maturity. Trees that survive can reach the greatest heights where guts have the most moisture, gentlest slopes, and greatest protection from storm winds. The islands' tallest trees, with some specimens over 30 meters (or nearly 100 feet), can be found in gallery moist forests. Because of flooding disturbances, differences in the forest layers are not as distinct as those in the upland moist evergreen forest zone; there are also fewer herbs, shrubs, epiphytes, and vines.

This large hog plum tree growing in a moist forest gut bears tart-sweet edible fruit.

Woolly fiber from the Kapok seed pods is inflammable and was once used as a mattress filling.

The islands' first human inhabitants, the AmerIndians, and later settlers used giant kapok trees (above) from the gallery forests to make canoes (left).

Effects of Disturbances

Heavy stormwater runoff and flash flooding damage and destroy vegetation. Careless land clearing by humans is even more damaging because it increases sediment and contaminant runoff through guts and into the sea. This runoff damages or kills freshwater fish and shrimp in gut pools, as well as coral reefs and fish populations in the sea. Poor land-clearing practices also reduce plant biodiversity, causing plant species to be less varied and numerous.

Damage to coral reef that has been smothered by sediment in stormwater is monitored by UVI marine biologists.

Guts: Freshwater Habitats in Peril

Freshwater shrimp from gut pool.

Guts are also freshwater habitats. Caribbean freshwater fish and shrimp can be found in gut pools and streams, including mullet, sleeper, eel, and goby fish species as well as shrimp species (*Macrobrachium heterochiru, Atya lanipes,* and *Atya innocous*), known locally as *langousta, cocuey, gut lobster,* or *kribishee*. They have complex life cycles, migrating between downstream marine waters and upstream freshwater habitats, and they fill unique ecological niches. For example, some freshwater shrimp (*Atya* spp.) filter stormwater by trapping organic debris with their modified claws. Various freshwater fish may either feed on small shrimp and insects or scrape algae off rocks. Eels (*Anguilla rostrata*) hunt at night because they have weak eyes but a well-developed sense of smell. The existence of freshwater fish and shrimp in Virgin Islands' guts is seriously threatened by projects that modify stream channels and discharge sediment and other contaminants into the guts.

Hikers explore Caledonia Gut on St. Croix.

VI Law Protects Vegetation in Guts

People unlawfully clear vegetation in guts even though these areas are protected by VI law.

VI Code (Title 12: Section 123) Conservation of Vegetation Adjacent to Watercourses prohibits cutting or injury to any tree or vegetation within 30 feet of the center of any natural watercourse or gut, or within 25 feet of the edge of a watercourse, whichever is greater.

Unlawfully cleared gut increases soil erosion.

BASIN MOIST FOREST
Generally 75% or more evergreen tree species

This panoramic view of St. John shows an example of the type of flat area at the base of hillsides (center of photo) where moist basin forests are typically found.

Location

Basin moist forest is found at sea level in protected valleys or flat areas along the coast, where rainwater runoff collects and drains from the hillsides. The word *basin*, which has several definitions, is generally defined as an entire watershed or drainage basin. However, in this case, the term *basin* means a flat area with a large or small surface depression.

Moist basin forest occurs in only two locations along St. Croix's northwest shore and in one place on Water Island's central north shore. It is more common on St. Thomas, mostly in the northwest, and most prevalent on St. John, where it is located downstream of the many drainage guts fanning out from the central upland areas.

Good examples:

St. Croix—Annaly Bay.

St. Thomas—Magens Bay (Arboretum) and Perseverance Bay.

St. John—Reef Bay, Coral Bay.

Water Island—near Elephant Bay.

Basin moist forest grows behind the wetlands at Perseverance Bay, St. Thomas.

Community Description

Most tree species are evergreen, but several of the tallest trees may be deciduous. The tallest trees in the basin moist forest may reach more than 25 meters (82 feet).

A native grass, *Olyra* latifolia, *grows to form a dense cover in the basin moist forest bottom layer at Perseverance Bay.*

Well-established moist basin forest normally has three layers:

Upper layer—A continuous tree canopy covers at 15–18 meters (49–59 feet) with some taller emergent trees reaching more than 25 meters tall (82 feet).

Middle layer—This layer ranges from 5 to 10 meters (16–33 feet), with a lower shrub layer that may be moderately well developed.

Bottom layer—An established basin moist forest may have significant numbers of herbs and vines. Epiphytes and ferns are rare.

*Some of the bigger trees in moist basin forest like this kapok (*Ceiba pentandra) *may develop buttressed roots for support.*

The rare bullettwood tree (Manilkara bidentata) is one of the taller trees (up to 100 feet) in the basin forest. It was once one of region's most commercially important timber trees.

Close-up of locally endangered tree, Erythrina eggersii, in moist basin forest.

Stormwater flow transports seeds from other locations to the moist basin, like the seed that gave rise to this locally endangered tree recently found at Magens Bay.

Effects of Disturbances

From the earliest human inhabitation of these islands, basin moist forest areas have been favored for settlements, cultivation, plantation development, and—in more modern times—hotel construction. Remnants of coconut palm (*Cocos nucifera*) groves and many other non-native plants have replaced much of the natural basin moist forest vegetation.

Loss of vegetative cover causes soil erosion in this zone, making it prone to flooding. Soils exposed to sunlight also become more impacted. Sun-loving weedy shrubs, herbs, grasses, and grasslike sedges can grow rapidly and crowd out the more shade-loving plant species that normally inhabit this zone when it is undisturbed. Vines can also become very aggressive, hindering tree growth.

Red outline shows cultivated coconut grove and moist basin forest at Magens Bay, St. Thomas.

Heavy clay soil excavated by land crabs in moist basin forest.

AmerIndians and colonial settlers once inhabited the moist basin forest behind Magens Bay. From the 1920s to 1947, the area was converted into an arboretum. Today, several of the tree species planted in the arboretum have spread aggressively, crowding out the native plant species that once grew in the basin forest there.

DRY FORESTS
of the Virgin Islands

These plant communities are defined as *forests* because the trees grow closely and form interlocking canopies. Dryness is more pronounced than in the moist forests, but enough moisture is available to support forest development. Dry forests are shorter than moist forests, generally limited to two canopy layers, and are usually found at lower elevations (under 300 meters [982 feet] altitude).

Factors that cause and influence Virgin Islands' dry forests are:
- prevailing, often strong, wind patterns;
- low moisture with possible dry season severity and length *(months with less than 50 millimeters [2 inches] of rainfall)*;
- sunnier and windier eastern or southern location and/or slope direction;
- degree of slope *(usually steep slopes)*;
- thin rocky soils; and
- heavy salt spray that contributes to reduced forest height, composition, and diversity.

Dry forests are divided into different zones based, in part, on the varying percentages of evergreen and deciduous trees. These zones share many of the same plant species, and it may be difficult to distinguish one zone from another. Dry forest zones include:

- *Semi-evergreen forest—Transitional type between moist and dry forests, with about 70%–75% evergreen trees.*
- *Semi-deciduous forest—Mixture of about 25% evergreen/75% deciduous trees.*
- *Drought-deciduous forest—Over 75% deciduous trees.*
- *Gallery semi-deciduous forest—In drier guts, with up to 75% deciduous trees.*

Dry Forest Cover in the U.S.V.I.

St. John (50.51%)

St. Thomas (43.01%)

St. Croix (9.22%)

Semi-deciduous forest on the hillsides behind the University of the Virgin Islands on St. Thomas.

STRATEGIES FOR SURVIVAL: *Trees and shrubs have differing leaf phenology or ways of responding to varying climatic conditions such as lack of moisture.*

Deciduous response
During the dry season when plants cannot continue to get water from roots, some plants go dormant and become deciduous by shedding all their leaves. Leaf pores (stomates) close, and leaves dry up and fall off. This strategy helps save energy and water by eliminating photosynthesis in leaves during stressful seasons.

Evergreen response
Other plants remain evergreen and do not drop their leaves. However, many dry evergreen plants thicken leaf tissue and reduce leaf size as adaptations to prevent moisture loss.

Deciduous orange manjack (Cordia rickseckeri)

Close-up of endemic fusic tree (Pictetia aculeata) with small, thick and spiny leaves adapted to dry conditions.

Some Virgin Islands' tree species are capable of being either deciduous or evergreen depending on their location.

*Black willy or Jamaican caper
(*Capparis cynophallophora*) is found
mostly in the dry coastal forests at sea
level and on lower slopes.*

A typical example of dry forest in the Virgin Islands showing the common turpentine or gumbo-limbo tree with copper-colored trunks.

Semi-evergreen forest grows below upland mois

rest on north-facing slopes near Caret Bay, St. Thomas

SEMI-EVERGREEN FOREST

Transitional between the moist and dry forests with about 70-75% evergreen tree species

Semi-evergreen forest on the upland slopes of Crown Mountain Road, near the four corners on St. Thomas.

Location

Semi-evergreen forest grows at the moistest extremes of the dry forest zones or at the edges of moist forests. This forest type is usually found at altitudes of about 300 meters (ca. 984 feet) and lower. It is located below upland moist forests on the central mountain peaks of St. John and St. Thomas, as well as on the slopes above St. John's northern bays and above 300 meters altitude on St. Croix's Mt. Eagle.

Good examples:

St. Croix—Mt. Eagle (north-facing slopes).

St. Thomas—Upper slopes below peaks of Mountaintop and Crown Mt. and connecting ridge.

St. John—Slopes above Trunk, Cinnamon, and Maho Bays.

Epiphytic "airplants" attached to rocks and several rare trees are among the unique plants found in the semi-evergreen forest on Mt. Eagle, St. Croix.

Careless road building practices caused the needless destruction of many trees in the semi-evergreen forest below Crown Mt. on St. Thomas.

Community Description

This forest cover type is transitional between the moist and dry forest types. Although it shares some of the same plant species as the upland moist forest, it is also very similar in distribution to the semi-deciduous forest type and, in many locations, grades or blends into it. Species composition changes to include a shift toward a greater majority (up to 75%) of evergreen species. Several tree species from the upland evergreen moist forest can also be found at the higher altitudes of the semi-evergreen forest, but they phase out at lower altitudes. In well-developed communities, structure may be similar to both upland moist forests and/or semi-deciduous forests, with either three or two forest layers.

Effects of Disturbances

Natural and human disturbances cause soil erosion, loss of soil fertility, less plant diversity, with the appearance of fewer desirable plants or weeds because the soil is unable to support the original vegetation. Wildlife habitats are also threatened, and drier conditions develop.

SEMI-DECIDUOUS FOREST
Generally about 25% evergreen and 75% deciduous tree species

This view overlooks St. Croix's northwestern coastal hills, which are dominated by semi-deciduous and semi-evergreen forest communities.

Location

This is currently the dominant forest cover in the Virgin Islands, including the remaining undeveloped land on St. John and St. Thomas. It is usually located on north-facing hillsides or upper southern-facing elevations below 250 meters (ca. 820 feet), along smaller guts, or in basins without large watersheds. It is also mixed with dry deciduous forests on lower south-facing slopes. This forest type possibly replaced a moister forest type that once grew on St. Croix's highest northwest coastal hills. A small patch on the southwest arm of Sprat Bay, Water Island, is the moistest vegetation type on that island, which is ordinarily dominated by dry thicket scrub.

Good examples:

St. Croix—Northwest coastal hills.

St. Thomas—Hillsides behind and to the south of Magens Bay and continuing westward to Fortuna.

St. John—Hillsides above Leinster Bay.

Water Island—Sprat Bay (southwest arm).

Community Description

Evergreen and deciduous species generally contribute 25% to 75% of the total tree cover. A number of fairly distinct and different examples of this forest type are present, varying in tree species composition, structure, and degree of human modification.

This forest type usually has two layers:

Upper layer—The continuous canopy is about 8–11 meters (ca. 26–36 feet) high with some taller trees reaching 15–20 meters (ca. 49–66 feet). A shorter form of this forest formation may have a main canopy about 6–7 meters (ca. 20–23 feet).

Bottom layer—The shrub and herb layer can be highly variable in this zone.

Example of bottom layer.

Semi-deciduous forest near Frenchman's Bay, St. Thomas.

Effects of Disturbances

Clearing of natural vegetative cover causes soil erosion and loss of soil fertility, drier conditions, wildlife habitat destruction, a loss of plant diversity, and weedier plant species, like the non-native tan-tan or wild tamarind (*Leucaena leucocephala*) and guinea grass (*Urochloa maxima*).

Tan-tan, guinea grass, and other introduced plants take over native dry forest habitats.

Wild anthuriums (Anthurium cordata and crenata) grow among exposed tree roots in St. John's dry forest.

*For just a few days, masse[...]
purple flowers bloom on [...]
wand-like branches of th[...]
small, endemic, native [...]
wattpama (Poitea florida) [...]*

Both the autograph or strangler fig tree (Clusea rosea, left) and native night-blooming cereus cactus (Hylocereus trigonatus, right) are able to grow on other trees.

Semi-deciduous forest grows on St. Thomas's southwest slopes from Crown Mountain, the island's highest mountain peak, to the sea. Much of this native forest reserve is now preserved by the University of the Virgin Islands.

Several guts transecting gallery semi-deciduous dry forest can be seen along Black Point Hill Road, St. Thomas.

Location

This forest type is only found on the larger islands (St. Croix, St. Thomas, and St. John) and is limited to the smaller guts and ravines found within watersheds dominated by dry forests on the main islands.

Good examples:

St. Thomas—Peterborg hillsides extending eastward to Harmony.

St. John—East end and southeast corner uplands.

Orchids, "air plants," and other epiphytes grow on deciduous evergreen trees and shrubs of the semi-deciduous gallery forest.

Community Description

This forest type is the same as semi-deciduous forest with the probability that trees may reach greater heights because of more moisture availability. Taller dry forest species find their maximum height in these locations because additional moisture is available as a result of runoff during rainstorms. Shrub and herb development varies.

Gallery forest along the Estate Adventure Trail on St. Croix.

Gallery semi-deciduous forest in a gut that passes through Contant, St. Thomas.

Gut pool at the Petroglyphs along Reef Bay Trail, St. John.

DROUGHT-DECIDUOUS DRY FOREST
Over 75% deciduous tree species

Trees that have begun to shed their leaves at the beginning of the dry season are evident in the drought-deciduous dry forest on south-facing slopes.

Location

Drought-deciduous forest is less common than semi-deciduous dry forest, with the largest amount on St. John and St. Thomas and a very small amount (less than 1%) on St. Croix and Water Island. This forest type is easier to detect during the dry season when leafless deciduous trees are easily seen. It is found at lower elevations below 250 meters (ca. 820 feet), on south- and southwest-facing slopes in drier east end locations, and on north shore south and west aspects.

Good examples:

St. Thomas—Peterborg hillsides extending eastward to Estate Harmony.

St. John—East end and southeast corner uplands.

Community Description

This forest type is dominated by 75% deciduous tree species like turpentine tree or gumbo limbo (*Bursera simaruba*) and mampoo (*Guapira fragrans*). It usually has two layers:

Upper layer—Main canopy averages 7–10 meters (ca. 23–33 feet), with a few taller trees to 15 meters (ca. 49 feet).
Lower layer—Shrubs sparse to abundant, and herb layer tends to die back during dry periods.

Deciduous trees that have shed their leaves during dry season grow on the dry coastal hillsides along the north side of Magen's Bay, St. Thomas.

*Water mampoo (*Pisonia subcordata *above), mampoo (*Guapira fragrans*), and turpentine or gumbo limbo (*Bursera simaruba *right) are some of the most noticeable deciduous trees in the Virgin Islands because of their large, undulating trunks.*

One of the Extremely Rare Plants in a U.S.V.I. Dry Forest

By Eleanor Gibney and Dr. Gary Ray

Among the most critically imperiled plants in the Virgin Islands' flora, *Solanum conocarpum* is an evergreen shrub in the Nightshade (Solanaceae) family. It was known by only five individuals in four locations until February 2003, when a population exceeding 183 specimens was discovered in a semi-arid section of St. John by David Hamada of the St. George's Village Botanical Garden.

Marron bacora (Solanum conocarpum)

Because of its extreme rarity, the require-ment by its flowers for out-crossing (fertilization requires separate individuals), and the lack of seedling production in the wild, *S. conocarpum* is vulnerable to sud-den extinction. Although flowering has been common in natural populations, only a single fruit containing a few seeds has ever been documented in the wild. Seeds have thin seed coats and are there-fore unlikely to be represented in the soil seed bank. No seedling recruitment has been observed from any of the five wild populations.

Little is known about the natural history of this species, including its reproductive biology and the effect of herbivory from arthropods, including soldier crabs that eat the fruit and destroy the seeds, or exotic browsing mammals, which abound inside and outside the National Park. Drs. Gary Ray and Alice Stanford are collabo-rating on an NPS-funded research that uses comprehensive genetic analyses, habitat profiles of the population and community structure, offsite propagation of hand-crossed offspring, and reintroduc-tion of seedlings into natural sites within the Virgin Islands National Park.

UVI student, Vanessa Forbes, collects pollen for research on Solanum's *reproductive biology.*

Our Rarest VI Plant Community
By Dr. Gary Ray

Dry forest formations of the Virgin Islands stretch from the coastal hedges of exposed headlands upslope to shrub communities, then intergrade with woodlands and closed-canopied forests on the higher slopes. A present-day oddity among these various communities is a "dry glade" or shrubland opening, discovered by Dr. Gary Ray and Eleanor Gibney on Little St. James Island south of St. Thomas in the early 1990s. Two other tiny relicts survive on St. John. These grassy glades harbor numerous low-growing species, including two orchids, several low-growing shrubs, and bromeliads, mixed with a few cactus species.

Rare native "glade" community dominated by Uniola virgata, *a native rhizomatous grass, develops on rocky coastal areas exposed to high winds. This site on St. John includes the terrestrial grass orchid,* Tetramicra canaliculata, *the butterfly orchid (*Psychilis macconelliae) *and other low-growing perennials.*

What makes the community unique is a combination of what ecologists have termed a "cryptogamic soil crust," which is a thin, cohesive coating of the top layer of soil occurring in gaps among the grasses clumps. These soil crusts are composed of lower biotic forms, such as cyanobacteria, algae, fungi, lichens, and mosses, all of which reproduce by spores or fission. The cyanobacteria fix atmospheric nitrogen, and the mycorrhizal fungi supply plants with phosphorous, thus amending and sustaining the nutrient balance of the soil. Particular species of fungi produce filaments that associate with the roots of orchid species, allowing them to gain critical nutrients. The soil crust prevents wind and water erosion, which would eliminate the fine soil particles, spores, and nutrients critical to the integrity of this extraordinary ecosystem. Dr. Ray has speculated that this community was once quite common, but was largely destroyed primarily by goat grazing in the region's small cays.

of the Virgin Islands

Woodlands can be broadly defined as land covered with woody vegetation. In this classification system, woodlands are specifically defined as vegetation communities with open or noninterlocking tree canopies covering 25% to 60% of the land.

Native palm groves or brakes are probably the only naturally occurring woodlands in the USVI. Most of the other communities classified as woodlands have been caused by human (anthropogenic) impacts such as agriculture and land clearing. The height of the open tree canopy varies greatly in woodlands, from 8–20 meters (ca. 26–67 feet),

Fruiting native teyer palms

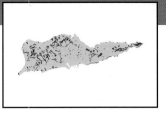

St. John (1.02%)   St. Thomas (2.42%)   St. Croix (5.43%)

depending on human impacts, animal grazing, effects of hurricanes, and available soil moisture.

Woodlands are also affected by the same factors that cause and influence Virgin Islands' dry forests, and many of the same plant species found in the dry forests are also found in woodland areas.

Woodlands are divided into different types based, in part, on the ratio of deciduous and evergreen trees in the open canopy cover. Types include:

Evergreen woodland—Native or non-native palm groves with broadleaf evergreen palms usually comprising about 75% of the canopy cover.

Semi-deciduous woodland—Communities in abandoned agricultural land or along the seaward shore of salt ponds with up to 75% deciduous trees.

Gallery semi-deciduous woodland—Communities in cleared areas bordering low elevation guts with up to 75% deciduous trees.

Drought-deciduous woodland—Patchy communities on drier eastern hills with more than 75% deciduous trees in the canopy cover.

Palm groves on the windswept slopes along St. Thomas's northern coast.

Location

Evergreen native teyer or tyre palm (*Cocothrinax alta*) woodlands grow in small patches near coastlines and hillsides from near sea level to an altitude a little over 305 meters (ca. 1000 feet) in both moist and dry forests. Patches or groves are established on St. John's and St. Thomas's northern and northwestern coastal hillsides at low elevations. Small patches also grow on St. Thomas's steeper northern slopes and some southwestern slopes, as well as on the northern side of Water Island. Teyer palm groves are scattered (and possibly naturalized) throughout St. Croix, mostly in conjunction with caliche (limestone) soils.

A teyer palm in St. John's dry forest.

Good examples:
St. Croix—Creque Dam and Caledonia Gut (various locations).
St. Thomas—Scattered patches along coast from Dorothea Bay and westward.
St. John—Northside of Mary Point.
Water Island—Northside.

Teyer palm grove.

Community Description

Natural evergreen (broadleaf) woodlands are formed almost exclusively of a single endemic native palm species, teyer palm. Mature teyer palms range from about 2 to 15 meters (ca. 7–50 feet). Groves can be densely populated with palms in various stages of growth. At the ground level, fallen palm leaves tend to discourage the growth of ground covers. Established palm groves can provide up to 60% land cover.

Effects of Disturbances

Teyer palms are endemic to the Virgin Islands and Puerto Rico, and their natural range is limited to this region. Many people have cut these palms during land clearing, thinking that the palms will regrow, but this type of palm does not regenerate when cut.

Teyer palm fruit provides food for birds.

Teyer Palm, Endemic Species of the Native Woodlands

Teyer palm (*Cocothrinax alta*) is an endemic species, meaning that its natural range is limited to the Virgin Islands and Puerto Rico.

The Virgin Islands and Puerto Rico are oceanic islands isolated from continents. This isolation has contributed to the existence of local and endemic plant species found nowhere else in the world. Many endemic plants of this region are also rare (occurring only in small numbers), endangered, or in immediate danger of extinction.

Teyer (or tyre) palm, also known as silver-palm, broom teyer, thatch or fan palm, has silvery leaves once highly valued for making roof thatch, hats, bags, and rope.

Teyer palm fruit is eaten by birds and was traditionally used as a fabric dye.

Webbing from teyer palm leaf sheath was once used to strain cassava.

Palm leaves were used to weave baskets and bags.

Teyer palms naturally grow in both moist forests (St. Thomas, left) near Caret Bay and dry forests (St. John, below).

Cultivated and Naturalized Palm Woodlands

Other evergreen palm woodlands were originally cultivated. Groves of non-native coconut palms (*Cocos nucifera*) and Puerto Rican hat palm or bull teyer (*Sabal casuarium*) can be found in moist basin coastal areas.

Planted coconut palm grove near beach.

Puerto Rican hat palms escaped cultivation and spread to coastal slopes.

A Puerto Rican hat palm (background) planted in Frenchtown, St. Thomas.

The Useful Puerto Rican Hat Palm

The majestic Puerto Rican Hat Palm, native to Puerto Rico, was originally cultivated in the Virgin Islands for its leaves, which are used to make hats and bags. After introduction, this palm spread spontaneously and can now be found growing in patches and groves along the north shore of coastal slopes on St. John and St. Thomas.

Photo by Diana Ulsamer

n the recent past, palm leaf weavers could be commonly seen in Frenchtown on St. Thomas.

SEMI-DECIDUOUS WOODLAND

Broadleaf evergreen palms usually comprise about 75% of the open canopy cover

Semi-deciduous woodland grows in the abandoned pastureland of central St. Thomas.

Location
This woodland type is found mostly on abandoned agricultural and pasture land throughout St. Croix's undeveloped areas. St. Croix's history favored large-scale crop production and animal grazing. These activities encouraged woodland development and discouraged regrowth of the native forests. Patches also exist in central and eastern St. Thomas, western Water Island, and southern St. John, typically in coastal habitats along the seaward shores of salt ponds and flats.

Community Description
The open tree canopy provides a 25%–60% land cover of common native, naturalized non-native, and exotic plants with up to 75% deciduous tree species. Tree size varies considerably, ranging from 5 to 25 meters (ca.16–82 feet) depending on past land use history.

Coastal woodland near Salt River, St. Croix.

Effects of Disturbances
These open woodland areas are especially prone to damage by hurricane winds, which reduce canopy cover and impact dependent plant and animal species.

Gallery woodland grows in a corridor along a ravine transecting hillsides dominated by grass on St. Croix.

Location

This woodland type, found primarily on St. Croix, is caused by extensive land clearing. It is located in guts and ravines at low elevations and appears as strips of open canopy woodland where guts pass through cleared areas.

Community Description

Although this woodland type is described the same as semi-deciduous forest, trees may reach greater heights because of more moisture availability.

Effects of Disturbances

Gallery woodlands are vital habitats for migrating songbirds. Reduction or removal of the canopy cover impacts bird populations and their movements.

Gallery woodland grows along a stream through cleared St. Croix countryside.

DROUGHT-DECIDUOUS WOODLAND
More than 75% deciduous trees in an open canopy

A patch of drought-deciduous woodland grows on St. Croix's drier east end.

Location
This woodland type occurs most commonly in patches on St. Croix's drier eastern hills and scattered elsewhere across the island.

Community Description
It can be difficult to distinguish drought-deciduous woodland from semi-deciduous woodland because species composition and community structure are very similar, with the exception that more tree species (over 75%) are deciduous.

This dramatic landscape (below) shows drought-deciduous woodland growing at the base of hillsides (center right) on St. Croix. Leafless deciduous trees are recognizable on the mid to upper slopes covered with drought-deciduous forest (left) and grading into shrubland (right). Thorny casha species growing in the foreground indicate that this landscape was disturbed and is recovering from a history of land clearing and grazing.

This view of a woodland near Butler Bay, St. Croix, shows a type of maintained and traditional pastoral landscape that can still be found on St. Croix.

Two silk cotton trees (Ceiba pentandra), *show their typical buttress roots.*

Shrublands are defined as communities dominated by multiple-stemmed, bushy, and often interlocking perennial woody plants of relatively low height. Shrubs usually comprise more than 25% and trees less than 25% of the total cover found in the USVI.

Shrublands are found in dry locations at low elevations on all of the USVI and on most offshore cays wherever conditions are harsher than those affecting forest and woodland formation. Vegetation height is limited by various extreme habitat features, including:

- Shallow rocky soils with low moisture retention.
- Impoverished and eroded soils caused by human land-use and grazing animals.
- Prevailing strong winds and salt spray.
- Intense sunlight exposure because of slope direction (aspect).

Different shrubland types can be similar in appearance and species composition, making it difficult to distinguish one type from another. Some shrubland types are also transitional and affected by how the land is used. Transitional communities can be replaced with a succession of other vegetation community types when land-use practices change.

St. John (25.57%)   St. Thomas (14.85%)   St. Croix (34.87%)

Shrubland types include the following:

Coastal hedge—Dense, salt-adapted, mostly evergreen (at least 75%) shrub communities shaped into hedge-like patches by the prevailing, shearing winds.
Sclerophyllous evergreen shrubland—Uncommon shrubland community type, similar to coastal hedge, usually dominated by over 75% evergreen plants with small, tough leaves.
Thicket/scrub—Very dense vegetation cover formed of interlocking plants, including several subtypes that range from natural to extremely degraded.
Mixed dry shrubland—Common shrubland formations with various compositions of deciduous and evergreen species, thorny shrub and cactus species, and other succulents that adapt to extremely dry conditions.
Gallery shrubland—Shrubland type of mixed evergreen-deciduous species (75%–25% each) found along smaller guts in dry areas.

Coastal hedge shrubland can be seen at Lindquist Beach, St. Thomas.

Salt-tolerant vegetation dominated by shrubs with thick and leathery leaves grows on the rocky coastal cliffs on Tropaco Point, St. Thomas.

View from Ram Head across Nanny Point, St. John, features patches of coastal hedge shrubland in the foreground. Tortola, British Virgin Islands, is in the far background.

This coastal hedge is composed of the fragrant maran bush (*Croton rigidus*, lower right), once used as an insect repellent; marble tree (*Cassine xylocarpa*, shrub behind maran), traditionally used for marble games; turk's cap cactus (*Melocactus intortus*), with the reddish crowning stems (midground) protected by VI law; and pipe organ cactus (*Pilosocereus royenii*, center background) endemic to Puerto Rico and the Virgin Islands.

Ram Head, St. John.

85

COASTAL HEDGE
Usually at least 75% evergreen species

Windswept coastal hedge on the northern coast of St. Thomas.

Location

This wind- and salt-adapted evergreen shrubland type is found on all islands and on most offshore cays in east, southeast, or northeast coastal areas where exposure to the prevailing easterly trade winds is greatest. It may occur on beach berms, sand substrates, seaward sides of salt ponds and flats, or above rocky coasts and coastal pavement.

Community Description

Shearing winds and salt spray inhibit the number of species and plant growth, creating a hedge effect and shaping plants into dense patch communities. Almost all of the plant species (ca. 75%) found in this shrubland type are evergreen and capable of greater height in less hostile environments. Harsh conditions limit the number of plant species to only those that can adapt to wind stress and salt spray. The severe environment causes some plants to produce small,

Good examples:

St. Croix—Jack and Isaacs Bays.
St. Thomas—Patches east of Trapaco Point; southeast coastal hillsides.
St. John—Ram Head.
Water Island—Southeast coast with many good local examples of this along rocky beaches and rugged shoreline.

Sclerophyllous leaves remain partially rigid when dryness causes wilting.

succulent, stiff and leathery or waxy evergreen leaves. Epiphytes, smaller cacti, and orchids may be found growing on rocks. Hedge height is usually uniform and ranges from very low, less than 1 meter to 3 meters tall (ca. 3–10 feet). An extremely dwarfed form of coastal hedge under 0.5 meters (ca. 1 1/2 feet) is also present.

Effects of Disturbances

Human and natural disturbance can cause loss of plant diversity, soil erosion and degraded soils, the appearance and dominance of weedy plants and increased dry conditions.

Turk's cap cactus (Melocactus intortus, bottom, center) and bull suckers cactus (Opuntia repens, right) grow with orchid (Psychilis macconnelliae, center) among rocks in coastal hedge.

Dwarf shrubland at Ram Head, St. John.

Land clearing in a coastal hedge zone caused native plants to be taken over by weedy plants like tan-tan (Leucaena leucocephala) and guinea grass (Urochloa maximum).

87

SCLEROPHYLLOUS EVERGREEN SHRUBLAND
Usually 75% or more evergreen species

The uncommon schlerophyllous coastal hedge grows at Drunk Bay, St. John.

Location

This shrubland type is uncommon, contributing less than 1% of the total vegetation cover on St. John, St. Thomas, and St. Croix. It forms small, narrow stands in low moisture areas along the coastlines in west and/or east locations. Slight changes in moisture regime and slope direction (aspect), along with thin soils, create conditions in which thicket/scrub and coastal hedge shrublands grade into sclerophyllous evergreen shrubland.

Good examples:

St. Croix—Coastal shrubland at Annaly Bay.
St. Thomas—Coastal shrubland bordering Sandy Bay (at Botany Bay).
St. John—Coastal shrubland at Mennebeck Bay (north end) or Drunk Bay.

Community Description

Plants exhibit a strong degree of sclerophylly; that is, hard cells within sclerophyllous leaves maintain a rigid structure when plant moisture is low instead of collapsing. Leaves are typically small. Evergreen species are more numerous than in coastal hedge, ranging from an evergreen-deciduous mix (25%–75% each) to over 75% evergreen species.

Sclerophyllous leaves.

Effects of Disturbances

Disturbance may cause the loss of extremely rare plant species growing in this zone.

Machaonia woodburyana—Rare Species, Endemic to the Virgin Islands

In dry shrublands, competition among plants and seedlings for space and limited moisture is fierce. One rare species found growing in this environment is *Machaonia woodburyana*, a member of the coffee family that is endemic to St. John, the only known place in the world where the species is found. Only several populations are known, one of which occurs on the east end of St. John in the uplands of Privateer Bay, where it has been mapped and assessed. As a rare plant of woodlands and coastal thickets, scientists and residents are working together to preserve the population. In its natural environment, its growth is dense, shrubby, and thorny, with branches that are buffeted by salty coastal winds and which die back periodically, sometimes looking more dead than alive. This is a narrowly distributed species that is threatened by human activities, since known existing populations are located outside of National Park boundaries.

Machaonia woodburyana *flower.*

THICKET/SCRUB

Ranging from 75% evergreen, to mixed evergreen-deciduous (25%-75% each), to over 75% drought-deciduous species

Mixed evergreen and deciduous thicket scrub grows on rocky cliffs in southern St. Thomas near the airport.

Location

Different types of thicket/scrub are quite diverse and common in the USVI and associated cays. Thicket/scrub ranges from less disturbed, naturally occurring shrubland in coastal areas to the more degraded drought-deciduous shrubland in abandoned pasturelands. These shrublands are usually found on south-facing slopes throughout St. Croix and in the east and south of St. Thomas and St. John.

Good examples:

St. Croix—Coastal shrubland at Sandy Point; abandoned pastures.
St. Thomas—Vegetation along west end of Magens Bay beach; hillsides north of WAPA.
St. John—Hillsides above Leinster Bay; dominant vegetation type at Ram Head.
Water Island—Dominant vegetation cover type.

Community Description

Thicket or scrub shrubland is formed of interlocking plants that generally form a very dense, closed vegetation cover. Thorny or spiny species and stunted, scrubby trees with multiple branches may be common. Various community types range widely from at least 75% evergreen, to mixed evergreen-deciduous (25%–75% each), or over 75% drought-deciduous (scrub) species.

Dense coastal thicket formed of evergreen shrubs grows in gravel along the Mary Bay, St. John, coast.

Coastal shrubland is usually composed of mostly native evergreen species with stiff, leathery, sclerophyllous leaves like sea grape (*Coccoloba uvifera*) and marble tree (*Cassine xylocarpa*). Drought-deciduous shrubland is dominated by a few aggressive weedy species such as the introduced tan-tan or wild tamarind (*Leucaena leucocephala*), maran bush (*Croton* spp.), lantana (*Lantana* spp.), thorny casha (*Acacia* spp.) and the introduced guinea grass (*Urochloa maximum*). Human influence and land-use history have greatly affected the distribution of drought-deciduous shrubland and; in many locations, this type may exist as a transitional stage that will eventually be replaced with taller woodland or dry forest types.

Marble tree

Maran

Lantana

The average vegetation height reaches 3 to 4 meters (ca. 10–13 feet) with or without an occasional taller tree growing above the continuous shrub layer. Evergreen dwarf thicket/scrub under 0.5 meters (1 1/2 feet) also exists. Communities can be dominated by one to a few plant species that grow to a uniform height. Communities dominated by tan-tan or wild tamarind are typically 4 to 5 meters tall (ca. 13–16 feet), with a few taller, woody trees that are remnants of the former forest.

A low thicket of shrubs and the columnar pipe organ cactus grow on the hills above Salt River, St. Croix.

In southeastern St. Thomas, a scrubby thicket of weedy and spiny plants like casha forms an impenetrable thicket in areas once cleared for pasture.

Some shrubland types are also transitional and impacted by how the land is used. Transitional communities can be replaced with a succession of other vegetation community types when land-use practices change.

GALLERY SHRUBLAND
Mixed evergreen-deciduous species (75%–25% each)

*Gallery shrubland in gut at Salt River, St. Croix,
shows possible hurricane damage.*

Location
This shrubland is found in dry areas along small guts and ravines where soil moisture is greater compared to drier areas beyond the water catchment zone.

Community Description
Mixed evergreen and deciduous species (ca. 75%–25% each) form this type of shrub cover. Evergreen species are more common and the vegetation height can also be taller than beyond the water catchment area where less moisture is available. Very dense shrub communities may form in these areas as a result of land clearing. Shrubland impacted by human influences may be transitional and have the potential to change to gallery woodland or forest types. Vegetation height can range from 1 to 10 meters (ca. 3–33 feet) depending on available moisture and disturbances.

Effects of Disturbances
Vegetation in this zone protects water quality by filtering sediment and absorbing other pollutants from stormwater runoff. Vegetation clearing threatens coastal waters and marine resources.

MIXED DRY SHRUBLAND

Ranging from 75% evergreen, to mixed evergreen-deciduous (25%–75% each), to over 75% drought-deciduous species

The stately tuna cactus (Opuntia rubescens) grows in undisturbed mixed dry shrubland beside Drunk Bay Pond, St. John

Location

This vegetation cover is found on the drier east and south shore headlands at low elevations, especially on St. Thomas and St. John, where poor soils and wind exposure reduce water availability. In some locations, mixed dry shrubland may be found as high as 275 meters (ca. 902 feet) above sea level on south-facing slopes.

Community Description

Mixed dry shrubland often occurs in scattered thickets of interlocking plants. Composition can be diverse, ranging from deciduous shrubland or scrub with up to 75% deciduous or mixed evergreen-deciduous species (ca. 25%–75% each), to

Good examples:

St. Croix—Jack and Isaacs Bays.
St. Thomas—Red Hook and Nadir hillsides.
St. John—Ram Head.
Water Island—Southeast coastal hillsides.

A rare species of pipe organ cactus (Stenocereus peruvianus) in flower.

evergreen subdesert shrubland, with at least 75% evergreen species in the shrub cover. The latter is characterized by the presence of plants, including thorn, cactus, and other succulent species, with xeromorphic (dry) characteristics that serve as protection against excessive water loss. The native agave or century plant (*Agave missionum*), pipe-organ cactus (*Pilosocereus royenii*), and other cacti are commonly scattered throughout this shrubland type.

Although vegetation height can range from 1 to 10 meters (ca. 3–33 feet) under slightly moister conditions, taller examples of this shrubland can form with the addition of some larger trees. The shorter examples are common in very exposed locations such as on the east sides of south shore headlands.

Evergreen sub-desert dwarf shrubland at Ram Head, St. John.

Mixed dry shrubland typically encountered along some roadsides in the east and south on St. John and St. Thomas.

The Century Plant–
A Unique Plant Endemic to the Virgin Islands That is Becoming Rarer Under the Siege of Exotic Insect Invaders

Agave missionum, known locally as century plant or karata, is a native species whose natural range is restricted to the Virgin Islands and Puerto Rico. It is a large plant with a huge rosette base of sharp, thick, leathery, and sharply pointed leaves adapted to the harsh, dry conditions of coastal thickets and dry rocky outcrops where it grows. Standing out like a natural "skyscraper" in the landscape, the giant flower stalk (panicle) can grow from 4 to 6 inches a day and up to 20 feet tall. It takes many years for the century plant to store enough energy to produce its spectacular flowering stalk. Yellow flowers appear on horizontal branches growing up the main stalk during the flowering period, which can last from 4 to 6 months.

The century plant is a "keystone" species upon which many other species depend. Numerous insect and bird species feed upon the flowers and nectar, pollinating by design. Flowers are replaced by either seed pods or small plants (bulbils) on the stalk that have the potential to develop into mature century plants. Eventually, the flower stalk turns brown and dries; then the seed pods open, and the seeds are dispersed by the wind. The parent plant dies after flowering once. The drying skeletons, often used by Virgin Islanders as traditional Christmas trees, are home to countless creatures during their lengthy decay.

Recently, a sisal weevil (*Scyphophorus acupunctatus*), native to Mexico, found its way to the Virgin Islands, most likely attached to imports of non-native ornamental agave and yucca plant species. This weevil devastated the local century plant population. Sisal weevil larvae bore galleries into the growing century plant, and adult weevils feed on the leaves and assist in the development of secondary fungal and bacterial rots that block the plant's circulation. As a result, the plant declines and dies, its leaves limply falling to the ground.

Weevil attack kills a century plant.

The sisal weevil's total life cycle takes 50 to 90 days, with four to five generations per year. Recent research indicates that males produce an aggregation pheromone (insect chemical) that draws other males and females to the plant, triggering a massive plant invasion. Initially, the sisal weevil had no known natural predators or biological controls in the Virgin Islands, causing an explosion in the weevil population and a threat to the wildlife species that depend on the century plant. Birds, insects, lizards, and other dependent species that rely on the century plant's seasonal flowers, fruits, and other plant products will dwindle also, reducing local diversity. Many century plants died before they could flower, further decreasing the numbers of this valuable keystone community resource.

Virgin Islands herbaceous (non-woody) communities are dominated by annual and perennial grasses that generally provide more than 50% of the total herbaceous cover and have less than 10% to 25% of shrubs and/or trees present.

Coastal grassland is the only local naturally occurring type of herbaceous community classified in this category. Other grasslands are caused by human activities associated with agriculture, grazing of livestock, or land clearing. Most of these types of grasslands are found on St. Croix, with a few on St. Thomas, St. John, and some of the cays used for animal grazing.

Herbaceous communities are classified as follows:

Coastal grassland—Naturally occurring native grasslands in coastal areas.
Pasture—Areas cleared, maintained and sometimes cultivated for animal grazing.
Pasture mixed scrub—Pasture areas no longer maintained, grazed only occasionally, and in a successional stage of recovery.
Mixed dry grassland—Abandoned pasture in a transitional stage of recovery that can be replaced with a succession of other vegetation community types (shrubland, woodland, or forest) if the land remains undisturbed.

Herbaceous Community Cover in the U.S.V.I.

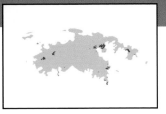
St. John (1.48%)

St. Thomas (1.93%)

St. Croix (18.23%)

Grasslands grow on the slopes above Salt River, St. Croix.

COASTAL GRASSLAND
Native grasses form at least 50% of the total cover

Native coastal grassland at Ram Head, St. John.

Location
Coastal native grassland communities are rare. Extremes of wind, salt spray, and low moisture sometimes combine to form communities of native grasses adapted to these harsh conditions. They may occur in widely scattered small patches on coastal headlands of the main islands and some of the cays.

Community Description
Both short and tall native grass species such as seashore rushgrass and dropseed (*Sporobolus* spp.) dominate with the possible presence of some other herbaceous plants (including succulents like talinum, *Talinum triangulare*) and various cacti (including turk's cap, *Melocactus intortus*). Shrubs (including maran, *Croton* spp.) and trees (such as mampoo, *Guapira fragrans,* and manjack, *Cordia* spp.) may also be part of the coastal grassland community. Mostly native grasses form at least 50% of the total vegetative cover. An open shrub layer and occasional trees may contribute less than 10% to 25% of total coverage.

Effects of Disturbances
The clearing of native grassland for construction further increases both the rarity of this beautiful grassland community type as well as diminishes the number of unique native grass species.

A native grass, Setaria setosa *grows on coastal cliffs at Ram Head.*

Coastal grassland communities naturally grow above the columnar trondjemite rock formations on LeDuck Island south of St. John. Animal grazing on some of the cays and smaller islands in the Virgin Islands group has also stimulated the growth of grasses and other low-growing vegetation.

Locally bred Senepol cattle graze on St. Croix pasture land.

Location

Most pastures are located on St. Croix, with only a small number of pastures in the eastern sections of St. John and St. Thomas.

Community Description

Pastures are areas that have been cleared, maintained, and sometimes culti-vated for animal grazing. Pasture grasslands are dominated by native and non-native grasses introduced as forage. Pastures are generally located on nearly flat or moderate slopes. They are often impacted by fires that are deliberately or accidentally set during the dry season, especially on St. Croix. Grasses are better adapted to fire and drought. Although fire favors grasses and herbs that can easily regenerate, it also kills many of the small woody species and prevents their recovery.

Grasslands may have small percentages of shrub species. Evergreen and semi-deciduous trees may also be present, including the native pink cedar tree (*Tabebuia heterophylla*) and the non-native guava (*Psidium guajava*). As in the past, the introduced guinea grass (*Urochloa maximum*) continues to be one of the main grasses cultivated for animal forage in the USVI, especially on St. Croix. Grass species contribute more than 50% of the total vegetation cover. Tree and shrub cover is usually less than 10% to a maximum of 25%.

PASTURE MIXED SCRUB
Grass species constitute more than 50% of the total cover

Pasture mixed scrub on St. Croix.

Location

This pasture type can form when pastureland is not routinely cultivated, is no longer maintained, and/or is only occasionally grazed. It is most common in drier locations throughout St. Croix, with some examples in eastern St. John and St. Thomas.

Community Description

This is a successional vegetative community type that results when more shrubs and trees are able to grow in pasture areas because grazing and fires have stopped. Pastures on dry and badly degraded slopes can be dominated by scrubby, woody plants that can tolerate these conditions, including spiny trees like thorny casha (*Acacia* spp.) and fustic (*Pictetia aculeata*); tan-tan (*Leucaena leucocephala*); weedy shrubs like lantana (*Lantana* spp.) and castor bean (*Ricinus communis*); and weedy herbs such as wild physic nut (*Jatropha gossypifolia*) and Mexican poppy (*Argemone mexicana*). Tree and shrub cover is usually from 10% to about 25%.

Casha, tan-tan, Mexican poppy, and other weedy plant species grow on soils degraded by grazing.

MIXED DRY GRASSLAND
Grass species constitute more than 50% of the total cover

Nonspiny tree species (background) are becoming established on abandoned or rarely used pastureland.

Location
This community type develops in abandoned pastures throughout St. Croix, with some examples in eastern St. John and St. Thomas.

Community Description
Successional changes can occur in the composition of the abandoned pasture vegetation community because grazing and fires have stopped. Mixed pasture scrub may develop into mixed dry grassland, a more advanced stage of recovery. Scrubby shrub and tree species that grow on more degraded pastures (classified as pasture mixed scrub) are replaced by nonspiny trees and shrubs like manjack (*Cordia alba*), guava (*Psidium guajava*), and croton (*Croton* spp.). This type of grassland may be transitional and eventually develop into shrubland, woodland, or forest. Tree and shrub cover is usually from 10% to about 25%.

Large open areas dominated by grasses are now found at island hotels, golf courses, and campuses (UVI St. Thomas campus).

A pastoral landscape on St. Croix has been shaped by this island's past and present agricultural land use. Great Pond is visible on the left, surrounded by agricultural lands.

Wetland communities can be described as seasonally, tidally, semipermanently, or permanently flooded vegetation communities. These vegetation communities are found near the coast in areas that are periodically or permanently flooded with salt-water and/or where freshwater collects from rainstorms. Areas of saltwater and freshwater inundation may be connected in complexes where different types of wetland vegetation communities exist in close proximity, creating rich wildlife habitats.

Wetland community structure varies widely, ranging from the relatively tall closed canopy of a mangrove forest formation up to 15 meters high (ca. 49 feet), to open salt ponds or flats and fresh pond wetlands dominated by low-growing herbaceous plants.

Types of wetlands vegetation communities found in the U.S. Virgin Islands are:
Mangroves—Semipermanently, seasonally, or tidally flooded evergreen vegetation formations growing in tidal area saltwater.
Mixed swamp—Tidally or semipermanently flooded areas with a mixture of mangrove and other wetland species.
Salt flat—Seasonally or tidally flooded areas surrounding mangroves and sandy coastal zones.
Salt ponds—Semipermanently flooded coastal ponds.
Fresh pond—Freshwater catchments naturally occurring or manmade.

St. Croix wetlands.

Wetland Community Cover in the U.S.V.I.

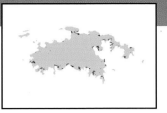

St. John (1.79%)

St. Thomas (1.48%)

St. Croix (2.22%)

Black mangrove grows along banks of the mangrove lagoon near Gallows Bay, St. Croix.

EFFECTS OF DISTURBANCES: Despite legal protection, mangrove wetland systems are often threatened.

Plant communities in the mangrove wetland system—including mangroves, mixed swamps, salt flats, and ponds—are protected by Virgin Islands law and recognized as vitally important. Despite this legal protection, however, plant communities in mangrove wetland systems are often threatened by land development pressures and activities. The vegetation is illegally cleared and ponds are drained to make way for development.

Virgin Islands wetlands are small in number and area, but they provide critical habits for many species. In addition, their ecological functions protect and influence adjacent marine communities. Mangrove wetland systems protect coastal waters and the marine environment by collecting and filtering stormwater runoff as well as capturing sediment from eroding soils and excess nutrients from sewage and fertilizer. By balancing the nutrient flow between land and sea, wetland systems also protect near-shore marine life, including seagrass beds, coral reefs and fisheries. Mangrove wetland systems are sheltered ecosystems that support fish and wildlife by providing breeding, rearing, and feeding grounds. In addition, over 90% of the indigenous and migratory birds in the Territory depend on wetlands for feeding, nesting, or roosting.

Juvenile fish swim among red mangrove roots.

More than 600 wetland communities can be found throughout the Virgin Islands, but the total land area covered by wetlands is relatively small. Many of the Territory's wetlands are manmade agricultural ponds on St. Croix and St. Thomas. On St. Thomas, wetlands occupy 270.48 acres or 1.48% of the island's total plant communities. St. Croix has 1,188 acres, representing 2.22% of the terrestrial communities; St. John, only 224 acres, representing 1.8% of the total cover. In general, mangroves and salt ponds are most common. Mixed swamps are very rare and natural freshwater ponds are almost nonexistent. Little is known about these freshwater ponds and mixed swamps, other than that they are used by many species of birds and other organisms.

Because of the steep terrain of the islands, the large and well-defined watersheds, and the small coastal embayments, land-use activities can have a significant impact on the quality of wetlands and surrounding waters. Hydrologically, many of the wetlands are seasonal environments; in turn, the duration of inundation and saturation, the salinity of the water, the pH, dissolved oxygen, turbidity, and influx of sediment and runoff contaminants create a very complex environment that supports a diverse and dependent community of organisms.

The overall changes in the USVI wetlands are disturbing. Many have been permanently altered or destroyed, as happened with Krause Lagoon on St. Croix and is currently happening with Mangrove Lagoon on St. Thomas. With less than 3% of the land area represented by wetlands and the increasing impact of both natural forces and human activities, remaining wetland acreage is threatened significantly.

During the last several decades, land development has increased dramatically, putting all existing wetlands at risk. They remain susceptible to shoreline development for tourist activities and water-dependent development. Degradation by sedimentation and septic tank leachate from upland areas is substantial but specific impacts are unknown.

In addition to the threats of human disturbance, mangrove forests in the Virgin Islands were heavily impacted by recent hurricanes in 1989, 1995, and 1996. Today they are in varying stages of recovery.

An iguana eats mangrove seedlings planted to restore hurricane-damaged mangroves at Magens Bay, St. Thomas.

Hurricane-damaged mangroves at Salt River, St. Croix

MANGROVES

Evergreen species generally contribute more than 75% of the total cover

The mangrove forest at Hull Bay, St. Thomas, flooded after several days of rain. Sediment runoff from uplands is evident in the turbidity of the water.

Location

Mangrove evergreen tree and shrub species grow in coastal habitats that are semipermanently, seasonally or tidally flooded by saltwater. Mangrove communities are found throughout tropical and subtropical regions of the world where the average air temperature is between about 66°F (19°C) and 107°F (42°C) and water temperatures are above 75°F (ca. 24°C) in the warmest month.

Good examples:

St. Croix—Salt River.
St. Thomas—Mangrove Lagoon Marine Sanctuary.
St. John—Hurricane Hole.

Magens Bay mangrove

Community Description

There are three main mangrove tree species in the Virgin Islands

- Red mangrove (*Rhizophora mangle*)
- Black mangrove (*Avicennia germinans*)
- White mangrove (*Laguncularia racemosa*)

Another tree, buttonwood (*Conocarpus erectus*), is often associated with mangrove formations.

Red mangrove grows at the water's edge and in the tidal zone where soil salinities range from 60 to 65 parts per thousand (ppt). Black mangrove is most tolerant of highly saline soil (90 ppt); however unlike red mangrove, its roots cannot tolerate being constantly submerged so it grows in drier areas. Black mangrove, white mangrove and buttonwood can grow near swampy areas and further inland where flooding occurs only during high tides. White mangrove reportedly has also been found in highly saline soil and is even less tolerant of constantly saturated soils than black mangrove. Buttonwood can also grow in dry soils and on rocky shores. Mangroves often grow in almost pure stands of one species or a mixture of mangrove species.

Red mangrove

Black mangrove

Mangroves are divided into different types:

Mangrove forests—The tallest mangrove formations, up to 15 meters (ca. 49 feet) and dominated by red mangrove, found in the moister parts of the islands where large watersheds drain into moist basins. Tree crowns generally form a closed canopy unless damaged by hurricanes.

Mangrove forest slowly recovering after being damaged by hurricanes.

Mangrove woodand

Mangrove woodland—Less densely wooded communities in drier areas where the tree canopy is not closed. This woodland type lies at the shoreward extreme of tidally flooded areas and may be dominated by black mangrove, white mangrove, and/or buttonwood.

Mangrove shrubland—Nontidal shrublands or scrub mangrove thickets dominated by red mangrove. It often occurs in the driest parts of the islands, is shorter, less than 5 meters (16 feet), and usually only 1/2–2 meters tall (1 1/2–7 feet), and sparser than mangrove forests and woodlands.

Mangrove shrubland

Fringing mangrove

Fringing mangrove—Coastal shoreline and salt pond vegetation that is semipermanently and tidally flooded.

Cattle egret in mangrove shallows.

A great egret at Salt Pond, St. Croix. Over 90% of the indigenous and migratory birds in the Territory use wetlands for feeding, nesting or roosting.

SURVIVAL: How Mangrove Trees and Shrubs Grow and Thrive in Salty Habitats and Flooded Soils

Mangrove species are halophytes (salt-loving) plants that thrive in salty conditions not tolerated by other plants. Although mangroves also grow well in freshwater, they have evolved in ways that allow them to survive in oxygen-deprived, waterlogged soils in habitats periodically flooded with saltwater. Tidal fluctuation may actually help mangroves by eliminating competition from other less salt-tolerant plants as well as further distributing mangrove populations. The following traits enable mangrove trees and shrubs to grow in salty habitats and flooded soils are:

Red mangrove stilt roots

Stilt roots—Elaborate aerial prop root structures allow plants to exchange oxygen in a waterlogged environment. These arching roots also support plants growing in a semi-liquid substrate or shifting sand (red mangrove).

Salt filtration—Salt is filtered out at the root surface. Saltwater is not taken internally by the plant. This occurs because transpiration at the leaf surface creates negative pressure, or a type of reverse osmosis, in the xylem of a plant's vascular system (primarily red mangrove, with white and black mangroves to a lesser degree).

Pneumatophores—Erect roots project above the soil surface or water level to allow oxygen exchange (black mangrove).

Black mangrove pneumatophores (roots) emerge above the water surface.

Salt excretion by special leaf glands—Glands on the leaf surface excrete excess salt. This results from a temperature-sensitive enzymatic process in the plant xylem (white and black mangroves, buttonwood, with red mangrove to a lesser degree).

Viviporous (live birth) propagules (seedlings)—Seeds germinate while still on the mother plant (red mangrove and other mangrove species in differing degrees).

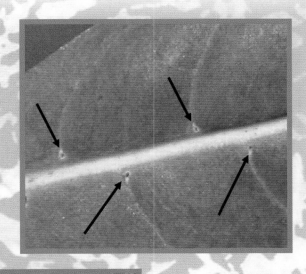

Arrows show leaf glands that excrete excess salt.

Red mangrove propagules.

Stormy weather can disperse floating propagules (example below) that wash up along the coast to start new mangrove communities.

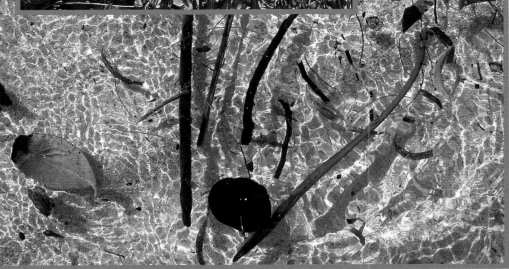

MIXED SWAMP

Evergreen species generally contribute more than 75% of the total cover

Mixed swamp along road to Coki Point Beach, St. Thomas.

Location

Mixed swamps are semipermanently and tidally flooded communities that form on the landward side of mangroves, especially where there is a large input of fresh water. This formation is very rare in the USVI, representing less than 1% of the total vegetative cover.

Good examples:

St. Croix—Patch near a salt pond to the west of Hess-Hovensa.

St. Thomas—Small patch along the road to Coki Beach, behind the Humane Society in Nadir.

Swamp apple tree

Community Description

Mixed swamps are composed of a mixture of mangrove species and a few additional unique and uncommon wetland species, such as the large swamp fern (*Acrostichum danaefolium*) and swamp or pond apple tree (*Annona glabra*) which is related to the popular fruit trees, soursop (*Annona muricata*) and sweetsop (*Annona squamosa*). A tree layer may

*Wet habitat plants like cattails (*Typha domingensis*) and grass-like* Cyperus *species grow in a small mixed swamp along the road to Coki Point Beach on St. Thomas.*

reach about 12 meters (39 feet) high. An understory of shrubs may be sparse, and the rare swamp fern may be present.

Effects of Disturbances

Despite its rarity, this vegetation community type is undervalued. Development threatens existing mixed swamp in unprotected areas. Because mixed swamps may be saturated or flooded for much of the year, many people consider them to be problem areas that should be filled in or drained.

Swamp fern can be over 3.5 meters (11 feet) high.

Mixed swamp near Magens Bay, St. Thomas.

In background: Swamp fern leaf (2/3 actual size).

117

SALT POND
Sparsely vegetated cover

Salt Pond at Ram Head, St. John.

Location

Salt ponds or semipermanently flooded coastal ponds have gradually formed in sheltered bays or inlets that were originally open to the sea. These areas became separated from the sea as coral reefs grew across the bay mouth and land development eventually followed. This occurred when fringing reefs grew upward, building a thin strip of land or berm from accumulating rubble. Mangrove communities growing in the rubble eventually closed off the bay from the sea.

On mountainous islands with irregular coastlines like the Virgin Islands, salt ponds usually form at the bottom of steep watershed areas where freshwater influx is heavy. The combination of mountainous topography and abundant coral reef found in the warm waters of the Virgin Islands produces this type of wetland formation. There are more than sixty (60) salt ponds in the USVI and adjacent cays; most are found on St. Croix and St. John, with smaller numbers on St. Thomas and Water Island.

Good examples:

St. Croix—Great Pond.

St. Thomas—Red Hook Pond.

St. John—Newfound Bay, Fortsberg and Europa Bay.

Community Description

Salt ponds are extremely variable environments. They are isolated from the sea and generally removed from tidal flushing. Salt-pond salinity goes up and down with inputs of fresh rainwater and saltwater coming through ground seepage. Pond evaporation or drying can increase salinity and salt levels. Plant life is more varied and abundant when salinity levels are lower. Shrubs and isolated herbs usually dominate. Salt ponds support mangrove species and other salt-tolerant plants, including the swamp apple tree (*Annona glabra*) and shrubs like cocoplum (*Chrysobalanus icaco*) and bay cedar (*Suriana maritima*), as well as salt-loving and succulent annual herbs like sea purslane (*Sesuvium portulacastrum*) and perennial grass species.

A solid or intermittent tree layer of mostly full-sized to stunted mangrove species is often present around salt ponds. Shrubs may grow among trees or as a shrub layer without trees. Low-growing herbs and prostrate herbs that blanket pond edges are common at the ground level.

Salt pond at Drunk Bay, St. John.

Salt-tolerant shrubs surround a salt pond on St. John.

What Causes the Red-brown Color and Sulphur Odor of Salt Ponds and Mangroves?

Red algae, microscopic plant forms, grow densely in the upper levels of the water where oxygen is more abundant. When the algae die, they sink along with sediment and sand to form a decaying mass. During the decaying process, aided by bacterial action, a sulfurous gas that smells like rotten eggs is released into the air.

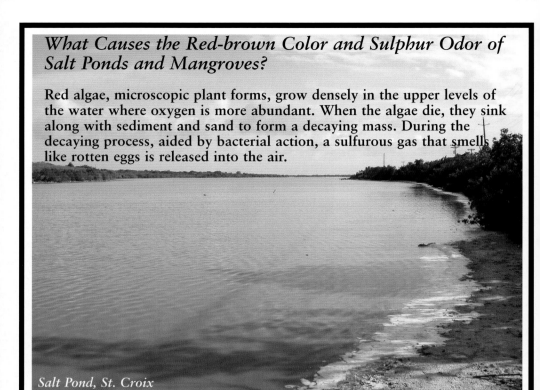

Salt Pond, St. Croix

Large salt ponds form in the flat area at the base of the hills behind Perseverance Bay, St. Thomas.

Land and Sea Link: Salt Pond Formation of Newfound Bay

Throughout the Virgin Islands and much of the Caribbean, salt ponds have been forming along the coast for thousands of years. Salt pond formation is a slow process. Coral reefs first grow across open bays, then storm material piles up and slowly closes the bay off from direct and constant contact with the sea. Over hundreds and thousands of years, the salt pond fills with sediments that have eroded from the surrounding hills of the watershed.

A salt pond (right) at Newfound Bay, St. John.

This picture of Newfound Bay, St. John, shows this process before and after. On the right is Newfound salt pond. Lead 210 tests show that this pond closed about 2,000 years ago. The pond is 4–5 feet deep with 3 inches of mucky bottom. Only plant species able to adapt to highly saline and acidic water can grow in or around this salty environment. Beside this pond, Newfound Bay is still navigable, but bay mouth reefs are clearly evident. Given time and healthy corals, this bay would also become a salt pond in thousands of years. The combination of salt pond, open bay, uplands, and offshore marine communities in this area creates a significant natural environment where diversity is high. Sibby Bay, to the left of Newfound Bay, is a small navigable bay with interesting reefs that is also slowly becoming a salt pond.

A land "bridge" across the opening of Newfound Bay caused the formation of this salt pond.

SALT FLAT
Sparsely vegetated cover

Salt flat near Coral Bay, St. John.

Location
Salt flats are level areas found behind mangroves, around coastal ponds, and sand or mud flats behind barrier beaches. Like mangroves, they are influenced by the sea and are seasonally or tidally flooded areas. They may also be covered with stormwater runoff during rainy season. Salt flats are primarily found on St. Croix, with some small patches on St. John.

Good examples:

St. Croix—Salt flat west of Hess-Hovensa.
St. Thomas—Patches near Mangrove Lagoon.
St. John—Hurricane Hole area.

Community Description
Salt flats are mature salt ponds that have collected sediment for thousands of years and filled in enough to eliminate surface water. As salt flats dry after being flooded, they support a flora of annual salt-loving plants.

Succulent herbs like sea purslane (*Sesuvium portulacastrum*) or less salt-loving succulent herbs with tiny leaves that form bright green mats on moist, slightly salty soil, like herb of grace (*Bacopa monnieri*) and the rare *Cypselia humifusa*, form mats on salt flats. Annual and perennial salt-tolerant grasses like beach grass (*Sporobolus virginicus*) and some shrubs also thrive in salt flats.

Sea purslane

Hermit or soldier crabs, unique wetland inhabitants, gather in a salt flat pool. These crabs protect their asymmetrical soft abdomens by occupying empty sea shells.

Small freshwater pond in central St. Thomas viewed from Wilmoth Rhymer Highway.

Location

Small, permanent freshwater catchments and drainage areas are associated with saline tidally or seasonally flooded areas throughout the USVI. These are usually found at the bases of drainage guts near coastal areas. Freshwater pond and wetland vegetation community types associated with naturally formed catchments comprise less than one percent (1%) in the USVI. The central interior freshwater collection basin on St. Thomas (Tutu Pond) was a fairly large freshwater pond, but it has converted to a freshwater wetland because of the heavy influx of sediment resulting from poor land-use practices.

Other freshwater ponds or wetlands are located in and around catchment areas of dammed guts, agricultural or golf course ponds, water troughs, open cisterns, standing pools in guts, and roadside ditches. Many of these are manmade, but they may nonetheless have value as patch or corridor habitats for many bird, insect, and plant species.

Community Description

Typical freshwater wetland plants grow in these ponds: cattails (*Typha domingensis*); duck weed (*Lemna aequinoctialis*), a floating herb that forms a bright green carpet in still water; water lettuce (*Pistia stratiotes*), a grasslike sedge species that grows in shallow pools and wet roadside ditches; and the rare swamp fern (*Acrostichum danaefolium*), sometimes found where water collects in guts.

Another view of the freshwater pond along Wilmoth Rhymer Highway shows cattails (Typha domingensis) *growing at the far edge of the water and providing shelter and nesting for aquatic birds. Water lilies* (Nymphaea spp.) *float on the pond's surface.*

Human Impact, the Greatest Threat to Salt Ponds and Freshwater Ponds—Vital Wildlife Habitats at Risk
By Carolyn A. Stengel

(from a Department of Planning and Natural Resources Division of Fish and Wildlife, EPA Wetlands Protection Report, 1998)

By far the greatest factor affecting loss of wetland habitat, in particular, the loss of salt ponds, is human impact. All salt ponds are coastal wetlands subject to extreme developmental pressure. As tourism and population in the USVI increases, the demand for more waterfront property increases. Restauranteurs and hoteliers look to wetlands and salt ponds because they are prime real estate locations. In addition, tourism boosts the need for more marinas and larger transportation facilities (ferry docks). Many of the coveted virgin waterfront properties are currently wetland areas.

Historically and currently, wetlands have been destroyed both legally and illegally despite federal laws mandating otherwise. Dredge and fill materials have been dumped into the salt ponds to create a foundation for homes, hotels, and restaurants. This destroys crucial habitats for local and migrant species of animals. The irrevocable damage not only affects wildlife within the salt-pond boundaries but also marine life as well. Coral reefs and seagrass beds are no longer protected as sedimentation flows unchecked into the ocean.

The last 50 years have seen a dramatic increase in commercial and private development. Wetland losses have also increased within the same time period. St. Thomas has experienced many salt pond losses as the direct result of development. The Wyndham Sugar Bay Resort sits on the remains of an old dump site, which previously was the location of several salt-ponds. A large two-hectare salt pond was filled in to create land on which to build the Cabrita Point condominium complex. Another salt pond at Vessup Bay was filled to create the road that leads to Latitude 18. Many other ponds have been opened to the sea, including Flamingo Bay on Water Island, Mandahl Pond on St. Thomas, Chocolate Hole North and Enighed Pond both on St. John, and what is now Sapphire Bay Resort Marina on St. Thomas.

The need for shoreline property conflicts with the need to conserve and preserve wetlands. With salt ponds playing such important roles as habitat, sedimentation basin, and flood control, the need to preserve and maintain these wetlands increases. Because salt ponds are the most numerous type of wetland in the USVI, maintaining them should take top priority.

Mandahl pond, St. Thomas.

Freshwater Ponds:
An Overlooked Resource for Wildlife
By Douglas Branch McNair

Many of the freshwater ponds in the USVI are manmade and presently comprise a total area of 52.2 ha (129 acres). Most ponds were constructed for livestock use in agricultural areas on St. Croix and less so on St. Thomas from the 1940s to the 1960s. Although some ponds in the USVI were filled to create housing developments, additional ponds have been created through golf course construction and sewage treatment facilities.

Wetlands and wildlife are intimately connected, and freshwater ponds are no exception. Yet they have been an overlooked resource for wildlife (especially birds) in the USVI. The availability of freshwater ponds, totaling about one-tenth of the area of salt ponds and mangrove wetlands, has helped offset the loss of some saltwater habitats. As coastal development has accelerated over the last 40–50 years, some bird species that require saltwater habitats have partially adapted to freshwater environments which are more numerous.

Pied-billed grebe nest.

Freshwater ponds are valuable to over 50 species of wetland birds on St. Croix, where fresh ponds are most numerous. The least grebe (*Tachybaptus dominicus*), an erratic and scarce breeding species, is actually more numerous on St. Thomas, where it occupies tiny freshwater ponds like the Bordeaux agricultural pond. The larger pied-billed grebe (*Podilymbus podiceps*) is more numerous on St. Croix, where it breeds at about ten freshwater ponds.

Common moorhen.

The most common bird on freshwater ponds on all islands is the common moorhen (*Gallinula chloropus*), known locally as red-seal coot. The number of moorhens, grebes, and other waterbirds at freshwater ponds usually changes in response to water-level fluctuations. White-cheeked pintail ducks (*Anas bahamensis*) respond most rapidly to changing water levels, although they will tolerate saltwater. Historically, moorhens, like resident pied-billed grebes, only occupied brackish salt ponds such as Southgate Pond on St. Croix when freshwater input was high and salinity levels were low. As a result of brackish habitat loss, these birds are using freshwater ponds to a larger extent.

Following severe droughts, pairs of white-cheeked pintail ducks (*Anas bahamensis*) occupy most rain-filled ponds, where they attempt to breed on the ground in grassland and scrub borders. Although pintails may nest in upland areas on cays, freshwater ponds have provided especially important breeding habitats to offset the loss or degradation of some brackish salt ponds, their preferred habitat. Many other important wetland birds, such as American and Caribbean coots (*Fulica americana* and *F. caribaea*, respectively), will also occupy freshwater ponds if conditions are appropriate. Management to stabilize water levels of freshwater ponds could substantially improve this habitat for wetland birds and other wildlife throughout the USVI.

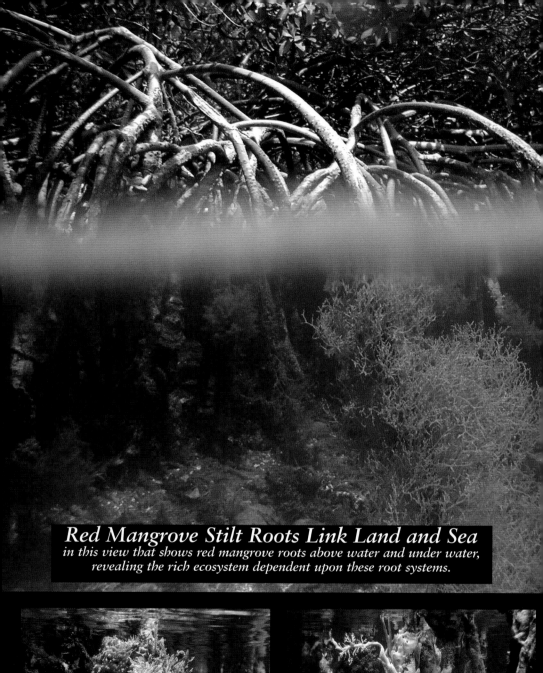

Red Mangrove Stilt Roots Link Land and Sea
in this view that shows red mangrove roots above water and under water,
revealing the rich ecosystem dependent upon these root systems.

Bivalves known as "mangrove oysters" cling to mangrove stilt roots (right of photo). Reportedly, the islands' early inhabitants, AmerIndians, harvested these shellfish as a staple food.

Red mangrove roots (above and left) serve as substrates for sponges, coral, shellfish, Halimeda spp. and other living organisms.

of the Virgin Islands

Location

Sparse vegetation communities with less than 10% vegetative cover inhabit areas that are quite inhospitable for plant growth. Physical characteristics of the landscape that limit vegetative cover include rockiness, lack of moisture, and hostile locations (e.g., coastal exposure).

Sparse vegetation grows on top of the brightly colored, hydrothermally altered rock cliffs near the St. Thomas airport.

Sparse Vegetation Community Cover in the U.S.V.I.

St. John (1.79%)

St. Thomas (1.52%)

St. Croix (0.29%)

A native cactus, "chickenet" (Hylocereus trigonatus), grows as a vine-like liana on a vertical rock slope.

Unusual plants like the fern Pityrogramma calomelanos *grow in the crevices of coastal rocks at Bordeaux Bay, St. Thomas.*

131

*Thick, exposed
roots of a
stunted button-
wood tree
(Conocarpus
erectus) climb
the cliff face at
Bordeaux Bay,
St. John.*

Sparsely vegetated tilted rock cliffs at Bordeaux Bay, St. Thomas.

This same stunted buttonwood tree may be quite old despite its dwarfed size.

An interesting collection of succulents including endemic (Agave) and cacti grow on the rock cliffs south of the St. Thomas airport.

Location

Rock pavement vegetation communities are confined to coastal cliffs, rocky outcrops, boulder fields, and landslide areas with less than 10% vegetative cover.

Good examples:

St. Croix—Annaly and northshore cliffs.

St. Thomas—Rock cliffs south of St. Thomas Airport.

St. John—Coastal cliffs at Ram Head.

Locally endangered cactus Mammillaria nivosa grows in rare colonies on barren rocky north shore slopes of St. John cays like Whistling, Henley, and Ramgoat.

Community Description

Trees and shrubs growing in rock crevices or between boulders often appear to be stunted, and the instability of landslide areas limits plant establishment. The plant diversity is usually low, and few plants can grow in these areas; however, unusual species and plant associations may be found. Many seabirds nest in the cliffs and rocky headlands where plant cover can provide shade and protection from predators.

The locally protected native orchid Psychilis macconnelliae *grows on the White Cliffs of St. John.*

Effects of Disturbances

A number of plants protected by Virgin Islands law, such as cacti and orchid species, as well as other unusual and rare plants grow on rock pavement. Plants growing in rock pavement habitats are threatened and destroyed by natural and human disturbances such as landslides, hurricane damage, and careless development practices.

Cobble beach at Drunk Bay, St. John.

Location

This vegetation type occurs on shoreline beaches of sand, cobble, or gravel and exhibits less than 10% coverage.

Community Description

Constantly changing beach shorelines provide very unstable growing conditions, although some plants are well adapted like beach pea (*Canavalia maritima*) and beach morning glory (*Ipomoea pes-caprae*). Sea turtles find this sparse beach vegetation good for building and hiding nests in berms away from the tide. Nests may be found beside patches of vegetation, where turtles push leaves and debris onto the nest to conceal it from predators.

Good examples:

St. Croix—Jack and Isaacs Bays—northshore.
St. Thomas—Fortuna Bay.
St. John—Drunk Bay, Salt Pond.

Hawksbill turtle nesting on cobble beach.

Effects of Disturbances

Destruction of sparse beach vegetative cover contributes to coastal erosion and loss of wildlife habitats.

Research plots at UVI's Agriculture Experiment Station on St. Croix.

Location

Cultivated croplands and farm plots are found mostly on St. Croix, with a few small farm plots on the north and northwest of St. Thomas and a few smaller home gardens on St. John.

Fruit tree production on St. Croix.

A watershed drainage basin is the area of land from the ridgeline to the sea that rain water flows across and under to drain into to a common shore outlet such as a gut mouth, pond, mangrove lagoon, beach or other coastal area. Watersheds contain ecologically connected habitats of diverse communities that are dependent upon one another. The landscape of each of the Virgin Islands is divided into many watersheds of various sizes, shapes and features. Within each watershed, all water runs downhill to the lowest point of land and eventually enters the sea.

Major watersheds can also be subdivided into smaller sub-watersheds. Large watersheds like Coral Bay (St. John - 3,003 acres), Benner Bay-Mangrove Lagoon (St. Thomas - 3,608 acres), and Great Pond (St. Croix - 1,999 acres) have many outlets to a common nearshore area, each draining an individual sub-watershed. Wetlands and bays found along the shores of these islands have a living connection with one another and with the entire watershed that drains into them. The largest watersheds in the Virgin Islands

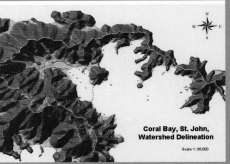

Coral Bay, St. John, Watershed Delineation
Scale 1:36,000

Coral Bay Watershed, St. John
Watersheds such as the Coral Bay watershed are defined by topography and the downhill flow of water. Topographic maps are used to delineate watershed boundaries. Downstream outlets and all major and minor water features (guts, ponds, wetlands) that eventually flow into the outlet are identified. High points (hills and ridges) are located by following topographic map contour lines. Watershed boundaries are delineated by drawing a line connecting the high points along ridges that divide one watershed from another. The watershed boundary lines cross slopes at right angles to contour lines.

are found on St. Croix Hovensa (8,135 acres) and Bethlehem (6,562 acres) watersheds have huge wetland systems at their base where they drain into the sea. These watersheds and the valuable wetlands within them have been highly disturbed by human activities, leaving fragments of the habitats that formerly existed.

Since all land within a watershed drains to a common outlet, any activity on that land will affect downstream areas of the watershed. Indiscriminate clearing of native forests and shrublands is a major cause of uncontrolled erosion in Virgin Islands' watersheds.

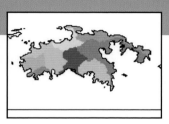

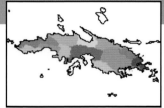

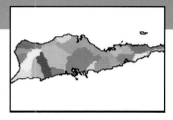

| St. John | St. Thomas | St. Croix |

Tropical watersheds are very important but poorly understood.

Management of complex tropical watershed forests requires an understanding of the physical and biological processes of these ecosystems and the natural and human disturbances that affect them. Many people living away from the shore and other wetland habitats do not realize that their land use activities will impact areas downstream and at the shore. These impacts are especially rapid and severe on steeply sloped islands with heavy rain events, such as the Virgin Islands.

As the rainwater moves, it picks up and carries away pollutants such as sediment, excess nutrients, bacteria and other pathogens, oil and grease, and other toxic materials. These pollutants are washed into guts, ponds, wetlands, ground water, and coastal waters where they increase turbidity, reduce sunlight penetration (slowing coral and seagrass growth), cause an imbalance in the natural nutrient cycle, clog fish gills, poison fish and shellfish, decrease fish, coral, and seagrass populations, and pose a human health hazard.

The vital connection between the land and sea is found between a watershed and the wetlands and bay that receive its drainage. Watersheds are now receiving attention from planners because their boundaries define identifiable ecological units, vegetative types, land-uses and impacts from pollution. People and businesses within the watershed have mutual interests in preserving the land, the sea and their quality of their lives.

Land and Sea Link
Coral Bay, St. John: Sediment, Reefs and Water Quality

Coral Bay, at 3,003 acres, is one of the largest watersheds in the USVI. This partially developed watershed had the highest growth rate in the USVI during the last census of 1990-2000. Typical of many bays in the Virgin Islands, seasonal rains frequently carry vast amounts of runoff water and sediment, nutrients, toxic substances and solid waste from the landscape and roadways into the Coral Bay.

A recent sediment deposition study conducted in Coral Bay using soil cores driven into the bottom shows an "impacted layer" of land-based material has been deposited within the last 100 years, more likely within the last 40 years as development has increased. Sediment deposition maps show current runoff and sediment deposition rates to be 7 times greater than in the past 5,000 years. Total organic carbon (TOC), a measure due in part to nutrient input from animal and human waste, is high in the central basin of the harbor. Reef assessments of nearby areas show low levels of live coral cover on adjacent reefs. Total suspended solids (TSS), a water pollution indicator, measured in Coral Bay are the highest in St. John. Outer bay areas in Hurricane Hole and Round Bay, part of the new VI Coral Reef National Monument, have also been negatively affected.

Coral Bay's pristine waters are muddied with sediment-laden stormwater runoff from road cuts in the watershed.

Right: UVI-Eckerd College research scientists collect sediment core samples to determine how stormwater runoff has affected Coral Bay.

Magens Bay Watershed - 1954.
Residential construction surrounding the bay is minimal. Bare slopes to the left of the bay, cleared for agricultural activity, impacted native forest resources, degraded soils and probably caused sediment runoff into the bay during rainstorms.

Magens Bay Watershed - 1999.
A dramatic increase in housing and road construction impacts unique native plant communities and jeopardizes the bay's water quality and marine resources.

Magens Bay, St. Thomas:
The Future of One of the Virgin Islands' Most Valuable Attractions Depends on Watershed Protection

The Magens Bay watershed, totaling about 1,100 acres, is made up of nine sub-watersheds that drain into five miles of coastline bordering the bay. Magens Bay, a world-famous tourist destination, has been designated as one of the territory's eighteen Areas of Particular Concern (APC) because of its highly valuable terrestrial and marine resources.

Over the past 20 years, development and land-use changes in the watershed's upland areas have threatened these valuable resources. Contamination from residential septic system discharges is suspected to be a problem that potentially threatens down-grade cisterns and the bay. According to the USVI Coastal Zone Management Program's (CZM) *APC Comprehensive Analytic Study* (1993) for Magens Bay, "The prime environmental hazard in the Magens Bay watershed is sediment runoff generated primarily from residential construction."

Sites are often cleared without any sediment or erosion control practices in place. Those practices that are used are installed improperly and/or inadequately, despite CZM requirements. Consequently, large sediment plumes following heavy rains are a common occurrence and result in the pollution of coastal waters and impacts on coral beds. Other watersheds throughout the USVI suffer similar problems.

(Above) a rapid increase in construction sites without adequate erosion control threatens Magens Bay.

Damage to the coral reef at Magens Bay is evident in this research area monitored by UVI marine biologists.

By Julie A. Wright

The U.S. Virgin Islands are in a state of rapid development, as evidenced by widespread housing, tourism, shopping mall, and road construction. Over 110,000 people live on only 130 square miles of land, with population density and development concentrated in urban centers and on less steep outlying areas, particularly on the dominantly mountainous islands of St. Thomas and St. John. However, as open areas are built out, development on St. Croix and St. Thomas is becoming more broadly distributed. On St. John, where the National Park Service owns most of the land, growth is accelerating outside of the park, particularly in Cruz Bay and Coral Bay, and on private in-holdings within park boundaries as well.

Charlotte Amalie, St. Thomas, and its surrounding hillsides are rapidly being urbanized. In this image, Charlotte Amalie Harbor is muddied by sediment runoff from upland construction sites.

Developed Areas in the U.S.V.I.

St. John

St. Thomas

St. Croix

Effects of Land Conversion

Development activities have caused ecosystem degradation, primarily through poor land clearing and landscaping practices that harm flora, wildlife, soil, water resources, and the local climate. Large-scale removal of vegetation reduces wildlife habitat, accelerates soil erosion and sedimentation, and threatens biological diversity. The impact of rapid development on coastal areas and the surrounding marine environment is of particular concern.

Sediment eroded from construction sites, dirt roads and other cleared areas is, by volume, the largest pollutant of coastal waters and the primary cause of coral reef degradation in the Virgin Islands.

Construction along the ridge lines of the Virgin Islands and in guts is rapidly depleting moist forest habitat and dramatically increasing impervious (paved) surface area. This increased paving decreases stormwater infiltration and increases stormwater runoff volume and velocity, leading to more severe flooding, erosion, and silting of coral reefs and seagrass beds. It is also changing the microclimate of the islands.

Many formerly moist forest areas have become hotter and drier, and guts that once flowed year round now only flow during rain storms. Chemicals in stormwater runoff from roads, parking lots, and other urbanized areas pollute coastal waters and impair coral growth, ultimately impacting Virgin Islands' fisheries.

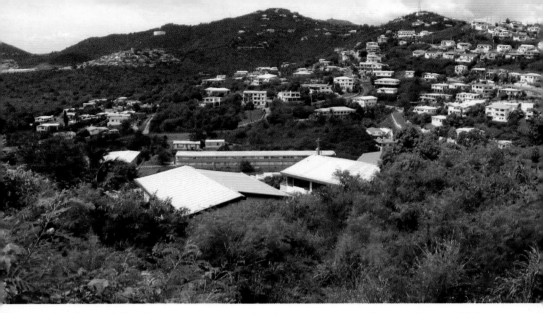

Poorly planned development or "sprawl" eliminates native forests that could be preserved in parks or green belts and used as recreational areas, noise and pollution buffers, and wildlife habitats.

Development resulted in the unnecessary clearing of large areas of native dry forest from these steep, rocky slopes. USVI dry forests are unique and fragile habitats where several rare and endangered plant species grow. These habitats do not seem to recover after the land is haphazardly cleared as shown above. Valuable top soils erode, reducing the soil fertility, and undermining housing construction foundations.

Site "fingerprinting" (above) reduces the total amount of disturbed area within a site by placing development away from environmentally sensitive areas (i.e., guts, wetlands, etc.). "Cluster" development concentrates building construction activity on a limited area of a site, leaving the remaining area undisturbed and preserving open "green space." Well-planned development preserves the natural landscape and incorporates much of the existing native vegetation in the overall design.

CRUISING IN PARADISE -
Striking a Balance Between Its Economic Benefits and Environmental Protection

St. Thomas is a prime destination for the Caribbean cruise market. Its beautiful harbor, fascinating architecture, beaches, and shops lured 878 cruise ships to St. Thomas's Havensight Wharf for a visit in 2003. Visits for the first quarter of 2004 are up by almost 25%. Although visitors to the USVI contribute heavily to the economy, this level of tourism can have negative impacts on the natural environment.

The cruise ship industry contributes billions of dollars to the international economy and creates hundreds of thousands of jobs. The industry is growing rapidly and so are the numbers and sizes of the ships. Several hundred cruise ships carry more than 10 million passengers a year around the world, bringing with them tremendous economic and environmental impacts. These "floating cities" range from one hundred to a thousand feet in length and can carry five thousand passengers and crew.

On a daily basis, these giant cruise ships can generate as much as 37,000 gallons of oily bilge water, 30,000 gallons of sewage, 250,000 gallons of gray water, 15 gallons of toxic chemicals, 20,000 gallons of ballast water carrying pathogens and invasive species, 7 tons of garbage, and the air pollution equivalent of thousands of automobiles. Moreover, these ships are not subject to the same Clean Water Act regulations that govern or apply to cities of a similar size (The Ocean Conservancy - 2003).

Marine resources in the USVI and elsewhere are at risk from many factors, usually associated with human activities of development or commerce. All marine communities, coral reefs, seagrass beds, and fringing mangrove wetlands are linked by water. Pollution from oil, sewage, gray water, sedimentation, toxic materials, and land or ship solid waste, along with the invasion by exotic nonnative species can have a negative impact on this fragile, beautiful, and complex web of life and eventually on that of the people who inhabit these islands. The cruise industry is vital to the economy of the USVI, yet changes must be made to reduce its impact on the very beauty that people come to see.

Below: Although tourism is the major industry in the USVI, the millions of visitors can negatively impact the natural envionment that draws them.

Plants That Grow in Virgin Islands Coastal Areas

There are several plant species that one may typically find on sandy beaches and rocky coastlines of the Virgin Islands. These coastal habitats and their plant communities may be classified as forests, woodlands, shrublands, or wetlands. These various plant communities share many of the same typical coastal plant species including those pictured here.

Marble Tree
(*Cassine xylocarpa*)

Pepper cilliment
(*Canella winterana*)

Sea Grape
(*Coccoloba uvifera*)

Jacquinia arborea

Fish poison
(*Piscidia carthagenensis*)

Black tea
(Argusia gnaphalodes)

Scaevola plumieri

Nickers
(Caesalpinia bonduc)

Bay marigold
(Borrichia arborescens)

Bay cedar
(Suriana maritima)

Sea purslane
(*Sesuvium portulacastrum*)

Spider lily
(*Hymenocallis caribaea*)

Beach morning glory
(*lpomoea pes-caprae*)

Pitcairnia angustifolia

Burgrass
(Cenchrus echinatus)

Frimbristylis cymosa

Heiti heiti
(Thespesia populnea)

Pipe organ cactus
(Pilosocereus royenii)

151

of the Virgin Islands

The Virgin Islands were physically connected to the former Puerto Rican Bank before the sea level rose about 5,000 years ago and separated the low peaks into the diversity of islands, cays, and rocks visible today. Thus, these islands often share similar physical and coastal characteristics:

- Limited coastline extension.
- Restricted coastal shelf.
- Permanent water temperature gradient.
- Oligotrophic or nutrient-poor waters.
- Scarcity of upwelling currents and zones.
- Steep, volcanic bedrock millions of years old.

Mennebeck Bay, St. John

Despite these limitations, or more likely because of them, the littoral or shallow coastal systems surrounding these islands are bursting with a biological diversity that is responsible for enormous marine productivity. The coastal shelf and adjacent coastal fringe support several important ecosystems, which include:

Above: Coral polyps are small colonial animals.

Right: Diverse spur and groove reef formation

- Coral reefs and other coral dominated communities.
- Marine plant communities dominated by algal plains, algal ridges, and seagrass beds.

Marine Community Classification

The classification of marine communities around the world, particularly in tropical regions, has not been finalized into an accepted standard as it has with terrestrial vegetation systems. As a result, the marine classification system developed for use in the Virgin Islands is specific to the biology of the coastal areas here and the needs of practicing scientists. However, this system is similar to the Benthic Habitats Classification system and other regional systems, used by the National Oceanic and Atmospheric Administration (NOAA), all of which allow data sharing and the ability to make comparisons between areas.

Fringing mangroves

Newfound Bay salt pond, St. John

Scientists have only a limited understanding of the complex ecological processes that occur within and among reefs and associated seagrass beds, mangrove forests, rocky coasts, and salt ponds, including the transfer of nutrients and the movement and behavior of cryptic organisms. Toss in emerging coral diseases, catastrophic hurricanes, and continued upland development, and the natural resource picture can become very bleak.

Seagrass beds

As the human population increases worldwide and especially here in the Virgin Islands, terrestrial and marine ecosystems are subjected to stress, disturbance, and change. Many forms of pollution, including water, air, and noise, along with inappropriate land uses, contribute to degradation and habitat loss, pushing many species and ecosystems to the point of extinction. Here in the U.S. Virgin Islands, the changes over the past several decades have been rapid, dramatic, and irreversible for the most part, threatening many of the values and resources we have all come to cherish.

School of blue tang

Deep reef

Zones of Life

Sparse vegetation zone gives way to coastal bedrock.

Deep reef zone.

Rocky intertidal zone of pavement and algae.

When looking closely at the changes in trees and plant cover while climbing mountains, or at the marine life while descending from the shore and rocky headlands out past reefs, one can see the natural differences in species, abundance, and distribution in different life zones. A moist forest at the peak gives way to a dry forest on the slopes, which becomes shrublands and then grasslands where rainfall is low. From the shore, tidal zones descend to a lagoon encircled by a shallow fringing reef, beyond which the sea deepens and slopes to the shelf edge. Many of the differences within these plant and animal communities are the result of varying environmental conditions faced by these organisms. These variable conditions—such as temperature, rainfall, light and aspect, oxygen level, nutrient content, salinity, wave action, exposure, soil type, bottom type, pH, and others—gradually change from ridge to reef, creating habitats for many species and forming a pattern of life zones.

The gradual nature of the changes in the environment can lead to a gradient in species, abundance, and distribution. To make it easier for us to understand, scientists refer to this gradient or pattern as habitat zonation. Altitude zones are common on taller mountains as dominant tree species change with elevation until reaching the tree line, a zone of dry and cold that trees cannot grow above. The zone changes climbing or diving are generally gradual, but the changes can be sharp for some species in extreme situations, like the rise and fall of the tide along a rocky shore.

In the sea, daily tides combined with water depth, bottom type, wave exposure, and many other factors form plant and animal zonation patterns common to rocky shores, sandy beaches, marshes, and coral reefs. The coral reefs are broken into three zones that show similar conditions, species, and composition. The back reef is shallow, calm, and protected. The reef crest is a shallow, exposed, high-energy wave area, and the fore reef zone has less wave action and descends deeper. The plants and animals found in each zone require the conditions found there, however, many are tolerant of a wide range of conditions and can be found in several zones even though their abundance may change. In the Virgin Islands, seagrass and some Starlet corals are found in shallow back reef lagoons. In deeper back reef areas, boulder and brain corals can be found. Elkhorn coral, which creates dense stands and thickets on shallow, high-energy reef crests, used to dominate this zone until hurricanes and disease devastated the population over the last 20 years. Now, more and more fire coral (ouch!) is replacing this keystone species. On the fore reef, in a deeper zone with less light and lower wave energy, brain and boulder corals plus more than 35 other species are present.

Ecological Interactions
By Dr. Caroline Rogers

By one estimate, one million different organisms are found on coral reefs, with only about 10% of them identified so far. These organisms are interrelated in complex ways through predation, competition, and symbiosis (a mutually beneficial association). Many of these relationships are not even known to science. Some of the more conspicuous interactions occur among reef fish, algae, and corals. Reef fish depend on reefs for food and shelter. In turn, reefs are affected by fish species that feed on macroalgae and algal turf (herbivores), and those that feed on coral polyps. Through their waste, fish also provide important nutrients, often a limited resource on coral reefs. Over 400 fish species can be found on coral reefs and nearby habitats in the VI. A recent inventory at Buck Island, St. Croix, that focused on smaller, more cryptic (hidden) species, found 225 species, including several new species of blennies, from this one small island.

Plant-eating (herbivorous) fish, such as parrotfish and surgeonfish, are abundant and conspicuous on VI reefs. Along with the long-spined black sea urchin (*Diadema antillarum*), they play a vital role in keeping the growth of seaweeds (algae) in check. Coral recruits (baby corals) need hard surfaces with little or no algae on them to settle and grow. The future of reefs in the USVI depends to a large degree on whether herbivores can remove algae at rates high enough for these young corals to survive. *Diadema* now appear to be increasing in the USVI, after over 90% of them died in the early 1980s from an unknown cause. However, they are still not as abundant as before, and intensive fishing continues to remove parrotfish and other important plant-eating species.

Damselfish, especially the three-spot damsel (*Stegastes planifrons*), are herbivorous fish that play a very different role from parrotfish and surgeonfish. They actually eat living coral tissue, especially from star and staghorn corals, and then cultivate algal gardens on the dead coral surfaces within their fiercely guarded territories. Depending on how numerous they are, they can either hinder or encourage coral recruitment.

Predatory snails eating elkhorn polyps.

Countless other interesting interactions occur among other reef organisms. For example, a recent study found that fireworms move from coral colony to coral colony, feeding on live coral tissue and spreading a bacterium that causes coral bleaching.

CORAL COMMUNITIES

of the Virgin Islands

Including coral reefs, patch reefs, colonized pavement, gorgonian dominated pavement, colonized bedrock and colonized beachrock.

General Location

Coral reefs are highly diverse and complex ecosystems composed of millions of tiny coral polyps that build the reef structure by building limestone skeletons around themselves. Most of the coral reefs around the Virgin Islands are shallow fringing reefs that parallel the islands' coastline. More than 40 coral species grow on these true reefs, hard pavement, submerged boulders, and rock ridges.

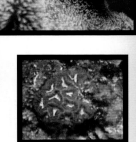

Bank reefs and spur and groove formations occur in deeper waters. Coral reefs support small island fisheries, protect the shoreline from erosion, create and nourish sandy beaches, and represent one of the most valuable coastal resources of the islands in the Caribbean. Although coral reefs generally have low biomass, they are highly productive and support a wide diversity of marine organisms, many of commercial or recreational importance.

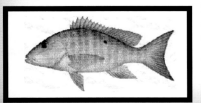

| St. John | St. Thomas | St. Croix |

These reefs provide shelter and food for most of the islands' fishes and marine invertebrates. Individual patch reefs and aggregate patch reef areas are scattered all around the islands and are abundant behind major reef formations. The best formed reefs are found in shallow waters surrounding these islands.

Bedrock reef

True reef

Coral Community Description

Coral communities occur as true reefs, built up by the deposition of carbonate materials from living coral animals and as coral communities built on hard marine pavement, bedrock, and beach rock. The composition of living organisms on the reef is highly diverse, one of the most diverse environments found on Earth. Each of the different classes supports a different composition of corals and other reef creatures. Many species are the same, although new species can enter the biological community and the dominance, and abundance of species can shift as well. The different classes of reefs in the Virgin Islands are based generally on structure.

Coral Community Structure

Coral polyps are tiny animals that commonly group together by the hundreds and thousands into colonies attached to hard bottom material, either by forming calcium carbonate from seawater or by cementing themselves to bedrock, beach rock, and hard pavement. These reef-building corals form massive skeletons in myriad shapes and sizes, honeycombed with tunnels, galleries, and caves, which provide more growing surface areas inside than on the exposed outside. Through million of years, a limestone framework has laid the foundation for tropical reefs, providing food and shelter for millions of associated creatures and building one of the most complex and fascinating environments on Earth.

Effects of Disturbance

Coral reefs are subject to many natural disturbances. Hurricanes frequently weaken reefs through physical destruction caused by storm wave activity, although

Coral head at Great Hans Lollick, St. Thomas.

Sediment plume in St. Thomas northside bays.

some coral species can reproduce from fragments. Sediment runoff from these storms and other intense tropical waves compound these problems. Higher than normal water temperatures and coral diseases also cause reef deterioration. Human activities such as coral collecting, boat anchoring and grounding damage, dredging, pollution, overfishing, and the negative effects of sedimentation caused by poor land use practices on steep slopes contribute greatly to coral reef habitat loss and degradation.

Driveway erosion in Coral Bay.

Land and Sea Link
Elkhorn Coral: A Species in Recovery or Decline?

Elkhorn coral (*Acropora palmata*) and staghorn coral (*Acropora cervicornis*) are the two major reef-building species of coral in Florida and the Caribbean in shallow coastal waters. They form dense thickets at intermediate and shallow depths, thereby providing a complex reef architecture that supports vast numbers of other marine organisms, advances reef growth and island formation, and affords coastal barrier protection and habitats for fisheries. Vast elkhorn reef areas that were healthy and thriving two decades ago have been decimated by storms, disease, habitat degradation, pollution, and disturbance. As a result, these corals have been nominated as candidates for the Endangered Species List, the first time a coral will have been listed. Recently, scientists have seen some limited evidence of recovery of the species, although they are still vulnerable to predation by coral-eating snails and fireworms. Research scientists at the U.S. Geological Survey (USGS), the University of the Virgin Islands (UVI), the Virgin Islands National Park (VINP), and The Ocean Conservancy (TOC) have begun a unique elkhorn population monitoring program using surface-water Global Positioning Systems (GPS) to accurately locate and record data about the health of hundreds of colonies. It is data and technical projects like these that help scientists and resource managers understand trends in marine populations and plan for assisting recovery through management and restoration.

A sea whip gracefully waves in the ocean currents.

Coral Sex: How Do They Do It?

By Dr. Caroline Rogers

Newcomers to coral reefs often confuse living corals with rocks. This is especially true in the daytime when the polyps of most corals are retracted. It is hard to imagine that these rocks are alive, and not only alive but animals that grow, feed, and breed. How corals breed is a fascinating subject.

Remember, just like rocks, corals cannot move. They are firmly attached to the bottom. An individual of the same species may not be close by. Because corals are animals and produce eggs and sperm (gametes), and the eggs and sperm must come together for fertilization to occur, the question is:

How DO they do it?

Many corals in the Caribbean broadcast spawn; that is, they release their gametes into the water column where they mingle and fertilization takes place. Because water currents carry the gametes away quickly, it is important that corals of the same species synchronize their spawning. To do this, many corals in the Caribbean only release gametes once or twice a year and only on certain nights. Spawning is highly predictable for a particular species. For example, boulder star corals (*Montastraea* spp.) usually spawn only twice a

Stony corals

year on the sixth or seventh nights after the full moon in August and September between about 9 pm and 10 pm. Their spawning is so predictable that dive companies in the Virgin Islands will advertise coral spawning night dives.

Synchronized spawning isn't the only way corals ensure that fertilization occurs. For many coral species, individual colonies produce both eggs and sperm. These colonies often release their eggs and sperm in gamete bundles. The sperm are carried to the surface by the buoyant, high fat content eggs, and the bundles then split apart. This is another mechanism for getting gametes in the same place (the surface of the water column) at the same time so that fertilization can take place.

For some species, such as pillar coral (*Dendrogyra cylindrus*) and finger coral (*Porites porites*), individual colonies are either male or female. Again, spawning is highly synchronized to ensure fertilization. Other species actually reproduce by holding fertilized eggs inside their polyps until they develop into full-fledged, ready to settle larvae. This mode of reproduction is common in the Caribbean. Many species that brood larvae do so for several months of the year (lettuce corals, *Agaricia agaricites*) or in some cases year round (golf ball coral, *Favia fragum*).

Monitoring for Coral Disease
By Jeff Miller

In the last several decades, the incidence of coral disease has risen dramatically. Currently, scientists believe that more than 30 diseases affect corals and only four of these have known pathogens associated with them. Black Band Disease, White Band Disease, White Pox, Plague, and many others are decimating over a hundred species of corals in 54 nations.

Diagnosing diseases in humans is a special science. Doctors and scientists perform meticulous tests to determine what is making a person ill, and what can be done about it. Is it a bacterial infection that antibiotics can cure? Is it a virus that will run its course with fluids and rest? Understanding diseases in coral reefs is much more difficult. The diagnostic tests are much more general; and, when we can determine what the disease is, there is no cure for any of the known coral diseases. Yet understanding how coral reefs are affected by disease, how much of it is dying, and what happens after a coral is diseased is vital to proper management of coral reefs.

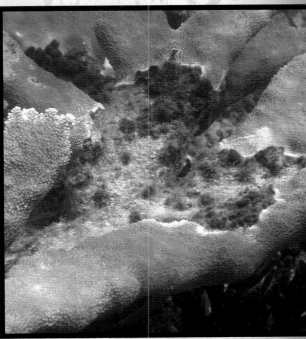

Elkhorn coral colony both diseased and eaten.

Scientists with the National Park Service in St. John have been monitoring the effects of the coral disease, Plague, at one of the most beautiful reefs in the Virgin Islands, Tektite Reef. This disease affects 18 corals species; it is very aggressive and commonly found on the primary reef-building species, small boulder star coral (*Montastraea annularis*). Monitoring monthly since December 1997, they have observed Plague-inflicted coral mortality at this reef each and every month. The extent of the disease does not seem to be correlated to season.

The rate of growth for small star coral is about three millimeters per year (in shallow water), less in deeper water. Yet Plague can kill the coral at a rate of centimeters to decimeters per month. When the coral is killed by plague, that area is usually overgrown by macroalgae, or seaweeds. After several years new coral may begin to grow over that area, but the new coral recruit is not commonly a major reef builder. The small star coral, with its slow growth rate, has yet to be observed re-growing over the diseased areas. These factors combine to make Plague a significant threat to Caribbean coral reefs.

CORAL REEFS:
fringing, bank, barrier and linear reefs

Location

Good Examples:

St. Croix—Buck Island, Turner Hole, Jack and Isaac Bays, Lang Bank.
St. Thomas—Saba and Flat Cays, Great Hans Lollick, Cow and Calf.
St. John—Newfound Bay, Hawksnest Bay, Waterlemon Cay.

Community Description

A **coral reef** is a hardened substrate of mounded relief formed by the deposition of calcium carbonate by reef-building corals and other organisms, relict or ongoing. This category includes the reef crest, back reef, and fore reef areas.

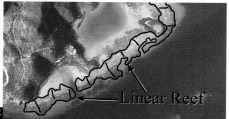

Linear Reef

The **reef crest** is the shallow and often emergent portion of the reef, usually colonized by fire coral (*Millepora* spp.) and other wave-resistant invertebrates and emergent coral. It is a high-energy wave area often visible in aerial images.

The **back reef** is that portion of the reef that is landward of the reef crest. Behind the back reef, shallow lagoons may form, creating a protected area. In some cases, the back reef slope to the bottom of the back reef lagoon is steep and composed of large interlocking pieces of dead elkhorn coral (*Acropora palmata*), which provide good shelter for the many species of fish found here. The

Elkhorn coral grows at the reef crest.

floor of the lagoon is usually sand and may be colonized with patches of seagrass, algae, and the upside-down jellyfish, *Cassiopeia frondosa*.

The **upper fore reef** habitat is sometimes found near shore, usually in the seaward shallow portions of fringing or barrier-type reefs from the reef crest to approximately 3 meters (10 feet) in depth. It is comprised of highly branching elkhorn coral (*A. palmata*), but other species may be present, including finger coral (*P. porites*), mustard hill coral (*P. astreoides*), lettuce coral (*A. agaricites*), brain coral (*Diploria* sp.), and fire coral (*Millepora* sp.) The predominance of elkhorn coral produces a structurally complex habitat with good capacity to act as refuge and shelter.

Staghorn coral

Finger coral

Brain coral

As a result of this complexity, this habitat serves as a principal daytime refuge for many species of fish that forage away from the reef at night in the adjacent seagrass beds and pavement areas (e.g., grunts and snappers). It may also be used at night by many species that rest here, hidden in the many crevices and caves.

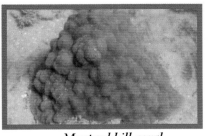

Mustard hill coral

Lower fore reef

The **lower fore reef** habitat is common around many islands and forms the seaward border of most reef systems where they descend into deeper water. Considerable variation exists within this habitat type. It can be found as an extremely dense, well-developed area of boulder star coral (*Montastraea annularis*) in a shallow bay, to a near vertical drop-off with high coral cover on the offshore edge of an extensive reef system. This habitat can be described as that portion of a reef having a high percentage of live coral cover, decreased gorgonian presence, and sometimes steep slopes to deeper shelf sand, seagrass, or algal plains.

Coral and sponge

The most common coral species are boulder star coral (*M. annularis*), great star coral (*M. cavernosa*), boulder brain coral (*Colpophyllia natans*), massive starlet coral (*Siderastrea siderea*), lettuce leaf coral (*Agaricia agaricites*), and brain coral (*Diploria* sp.). In shallow areas where light penetration is good, the head corals can form large domed colonies with overhangs that produce good shelter for fish and lobster. In deeper areas, boulder star coral colonies tend to be flattened to maximize light capture. The steeper slopes in the deeper portions of this habitat are generally more eroded and have numerous crevices and overhangs, which also provide good shelter for many species.

Brain coral

Land and Sea Link
Sea Fan Disease "Aspergillosis"

In another connection between the land and the sea, scientists suspect that changes in and drying of the climate of Sahara Africa has caused more dust, microbes, and pathogens to blow here along with dust from desert and agricultural soils. One such organism, a fungal pathogen called *Aspergillus sydowii*, has been found in air samples and has been identified as the cause of the disease affecting sea fans (*Gorgonia* sp.). No one can yet say whether the disease originated with dust from the air or soil from the land. On the other hand, many scientists think that other unidentified pathogens, bacteria, fungi and viruses commonly found in runoff waters may be responsible for some of the more than 30 existing coral diseases that are decimating populations worldwide.

Sahara dust

Common Sea Fan

PATCH REEFS AND PATCH REEF AGGREGATES

Location

Good examples:

St. Croix—Tague Bay, Half-Penny Bay, Great Pond Bay.

St. Thomas—Grass Cay, Smith Bay, Sprat Bay.

St. John—Turner Point, LeDuck Island, Hawksnest Bay, Reef Bay.

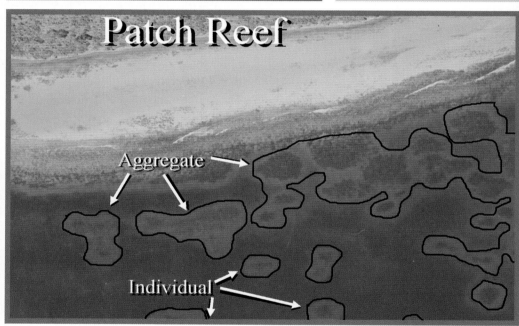

NOAA map 1999

Community Description

A patch reef is commonly a small reef isolated from shore and other reef systems by sand, seagrasses, or hard bottom. They can range from an actively growing shallow reef less than 3 meters (10 feet) deep and just a few meters in diameter, to an actively growing deeper reef at 10 meters (32 feet) and tens of meters in diameter. These patch reefs commonly share the characteristic of being an island of structural and biological complexity in the middle of an area of flat featureless

Patch reef with sand halo.

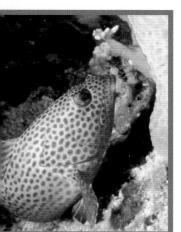

*Red hind juvenile
on small patch reef.*

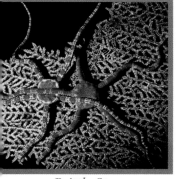

Brittle Stars

bottom. Fish are attracted to them for shelter and food. Many fish species may venture off the reef at night to forage in the surrounding sand, seagrass, or algal flats. Foraging by fish and feeding by invertebrates is thought to maintain a sand zone ("halo") around patch reefs that are situated in seagrass beds or algal plains. This very distinctive feature aids in the identification of patch reefs from aerial photographs.

Clusters of reef or patch reef aggregates in an area provide habitat diversity and connectivity between similar patches for species that are mobile. Larger, deeper patch reefs and haystacks usually have lower structural complexity on the upper surface, which may be sparsely colonized compared with the nearly vertical sides. The sessile invertebrate communities on these reefs are commonly of a deeper water composition, similar to what is found on a lower fore reef. Dominant species of corals include boulder star coral (*Montastraea annularis*), great star coral (*M. cavernosa*), boulder brain coral (*Colpophyllia natans*), lettuce leaf coral (*Agaricia agaricites*) massive starlet coral (*Siderastrea siderea*), brain coral (*Diploria* sp.), and pencil coral (*Madracis* sp.). The percentage of living cover can be quite high (60%–70%), with few gorgonians.

COLONIZED HARD PAVEMENT

Location

Diverse hard pavement community

Common hard pavement bottom type

Community Description

Carbonate pavement can be described as any flat, hard, carbonate bottom having a low percentage of live cover of corals and other sessile invertebrates (5%–10 %). Sessile organisms characteristic of this habitat include boulder star coral (*M. annularis*), mustard hill coral (*P. astreoides*), massive

Colonized hard pavement

Sea plumes and sea whips are common on hard pavement.

starlet coral (*Siderastrea siderea*), brain coral (*Diploria* sp.), many gorgonian species and others. Portions of this habitat may be covered by a thin sand veneer and appear to be sand with occasional coral or gorgonian outcroppings. Upraised portions of the carbonate substrate may be colonized by algal turf. Low structural complexity may result in low numbers of fish found in this habitat. Trap studies indicate the greatest number of fish per trap in this habitat, perhaps as a result of the vertical relief offered by gorgonian cover. In colonized areas, the surface of the pavement has a cover of macroalgae, hard coral, gorgonians, and other sessile invertebrates that will obscure the underlying carbonate rock.

This habitat type is found in many locations. Many shallow bays have pavement areas within them not associated with any adjacent reef systems (e.g., Cinnamon Bay, St. John). Many reef areas have significant amounts of this habitat type along the fore reef between the upper and the lower fore reefs where the slope of the reef is gradual and the coral and other sessile invertebrate cover is low (e.g., Johnson's Reef, north, St. John). Significant amounts of this habitat type occur on insular shelves seaward of any nearshore reef systems. This habitat has raised ridge areas, which are undercut to form ledges that provide shelter for fish and lobsters.

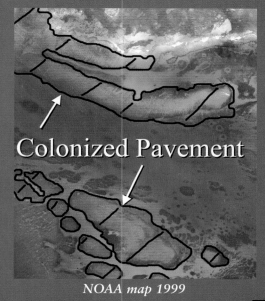

Colonized Pavement

NOAA map 1999

GORGONIAN DOMINATED PAVEMENT

Location

These areas are found in similar locations to hard pavement, except the pavement areas are dominated by common gorgonians.

Good examples:

St. Croix—Buck Island fore reef.
St. Thomas—Magens Bay, Mandahl Bay.
St. John—Long Point, Round Bay, Cinnamon Bay.

Gorgonians, commonly called soft corals, are plentiful in many areas.

Community Description

These hard pavement habitat types are distinguished from other hard pavement areas as having abundant gorgonian cover and reduced coral cover. They generally occur in areas of high current, presumably because the high transport of particulate matter and nutrients provides a rich source for the filter-feeding

Sea rod

Sea rod with polyps extended.

gorgonians. The low structural complexity of the gorgonians provides little shelter for fish, yet trap studies indicate greater diversity than expected. This may be an artifact of the traps concentrating fish because they add to the complexity of the seascape.

This habitat type can occur on reefs in high current locations in the area that would otherwise be carbonate pavement. It also occurs on pavement areas between small islands where current velocities are very high. Common species of gorgonians, which lack a hard, rigid, permanent skeleton, include sea rods (*Plexaura* spp.), sea whips (*Pterogorgia* spp.), sea plumes (*Pseudopterogorgia* spp.) and sea fans (*Gorgonia* sp.).

Sea plumes are multiply branched.

Sea plume with polyps extended.

COLONIZED BEDROCK

Location

Good examples:

    St. Croix—Salt River, Annaly Bay, Butler Bay.
    St. Thomas—Botany Bay, Bordeaux Bay, Great St. James.
    St. John—Whistling Cay, Waterlemon Cay, Pelican Rock.

Colonized bedrock is a very common habitat type owing to the geology of the coastline.

Community Description

Significant portions of the USVI coastlines are fringed by this habitat. It is primarily composed of exposed and eroded bedrock that underlies the adjacent island coastline. This zone generally ranges in depth from 0 to 3 meters (to 10 feet) but in some cases it can be found deeper. On colonized submerged bedrock, coverage of macroalgae, hard coral, gorgonians and other sessile invertebrates are abundant enough to obscure the underlying rock. The most abundant invertebrates present include fire coral (*Millepora* sp.), mustard hill coral (*P. astreoides*), elkhorn coral (*A. palmata*), boulder star coral (*M. annularis*), knobby brain coral (*Diploria clivosa*), symmetrical brain coral (*D. strigosa*), pillar coral (*Dendrogyra cylindrus*), and massive starlet coral (*Siderastrea siderea*). Gorgonians, fire coral, and sponges are generally also present. Live coral cover in this zone is commonly very low. Examples of this habitat type are found along most rocky shores, especially points and rocky peninsulas.

Elkhorn coral commonly grows on bedrock as well as true reefs.

Rocky cliff above colonized bedrock.

Many diverse gorgonians are found on bedrock.

Location

Community Description

Tidal and subtidal beach rock, gravel, or cobble of varying sizes are present along the coast, usually on many high-energy beach areas. It may be composed of loose rock and/or carbonate cemented and chemically bonded sand grains

The cobble beach at Privateer Bay, St. John.

and pieces of coral and rock. The rock diameter is usually less than 30 centimeters (12 inches), but they can grade into tidal and subtidal bedrock types. This may be gravel from degraded or carbonate "beach rock" that forms as a result of chemical precipitate and acts as a natural armoring on many high-energy beaches.

More than 600 species of Caribbean reef plants grow in these communities and on coral reefs. However, the vast plant life located in this region has not yet been thoroughly documented. The first taxonomists (Agardh, 1820; Montagne, 1842; Borgesen, 1913–20) in the Virgin Islands characterized the families and species. Since then, many others have furthered these classification efforts. The importance of reef plants to reef ecology and reef building cannot be overstated. They are the less obvious keystone upon which the reef depends for photosynthesis.

These populations can have a canopy height from a few centimeters (inches) to over a meter (3 feet). Caribbean reef plants, the seagrasses previously described, and algae form the base of the marine food chain. During photosynthesis, they produce food and oxygen, which is then available to sustain other organisms. Requiring sunlight, these plant communities are commonly found intertidally and to depths of 30 meters (100 feet). Some unusual species grow deeper. Marine plants like seagrasses have true roots and—like land plants—stems, leaves and flowers. Algae, however, attach by holdfasts. They both possess chlorophyll for photosynthesis. The algal community is dominated by microscopic phytoplankton or "plant drifters" but there are a number of other floaters, like sargassum seaweed, that use gas-filled bladders.

SEAGRASS BEDS

Location

Community Description

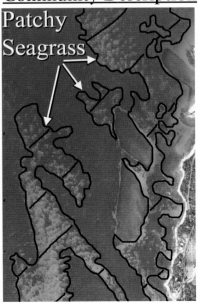

Patchy Seagrass

NOAA map 1999.

Tropical Atlantic seagrass beds, composed predominantly of turtle (*Thalassia testudinum*) and manatee grass (*Syringodium filiforme*), have some of the highest primary productivity rates of all natural systems in the world. They are flowering plants with leaves generally covered with marine growth or clinging sediment. Any of three Caribbean seagrass species (midrib seagrass, *Halophila baillonis*) may form isolated patches or vast monotypic or mixed beds at depths of 0 to 10 meters (0 to 35 feet), depending on water quality, the nature of the substrate, wave energy, and the geomorphology of the coast.

Seagrasses greatly modify the physical, chemical, and geological properties of coastal areas. They have extensive root systems that are well anchored by runners. These grass beds provide nutrients, sustain coastal fishery resources via

St. John   St. Thomas   St. Croix

primary productivity as plant biomass and habitat, create foraging grounds for endangered species, and enhance biological diversity. Seagrass beds also have characteristic fish populations and sometimes serve as nurseries for young reef organisms. Finally, these beds serve as important grazing areas for green turtles.

Seagrass community showing storm blowout.

In many areas, hurricane waves cause extensive blowouts of beds along with destruction by anchors and mooring chains. Seagrass beds and coral reefs have suffered from siltation caused by careless land-use practices, dredge and fill operations, and marina construction. The high turbidity and silty covering caused by these activities can decrease the depth limit of seagrass colonization, reduce light for growth, and perhaps make the seagrasses less palatable to herbivores like endangered sea turtles.

Seagrasses on sand substrate.

Many shallow bays, generally protected from oceanic swells, have sand bottoms colonized by marine angiosperms. Commonly, the communities consist of mixed stands of several species of seagrass, including turtle grass (*Thalassia testudinum*), manatee grass (*Syringodium filiforme*), *Ruppia* spp., and *Halodule wrightii*. Deeper areas may include midrib seagrass (*Halophila*). Other species of algae may also be present including lettuce leaf alga (*Halimeda* spp.), bristle brush (*Penicillus* spp.), green grape alga (*Caulerpa* spp.) and others. The seagrass bed category may be further broken down by species composition.

A rich, thick seagrass community.

An uncommon species of finger coral is the blue form of Porites branneri.

ALGAL PLAIN

Location and Community Description

Good examples: St. Croix: South shore.
Not commonly found around St. Thomas and St. John.

Algal plains are one of the predominant habitat types covering the insular shelf regions at depths generally exceeding 20 meters (65 feet). Green algae are the most common type found abundantly on tropical reefs. Many are calcareous,

Flat-top Bristle Brush, Penicillus pyriformis.

adding significant amounts of calcium carbonate to the reefs. The algae grow as single-celled bubble, blade, brush, and fan-shaped forms. Chlorophyll provides colors in varying shades of green and yellow. Browns and reds are also abundant on reefs and can be found as a mixed community on algal plains.

Associated with these algal communities is a substrate composed of carbonate algal nodules, which range in size from less than one centimeter (1/2 inch) to greater than ten centimeters (4 inches), and some sand. Few large fish are found in this community. Scientsts think that this region may be a habitat type for juvenile queen triggerfish. Examples of this habitat type are found anywhere on the insular shelves.

The Genus Caulerpa *is one of the more common groups of marine algae.*

Algal Plain in the U.S.V.I.

St. John

St. Thomas

St. Croix

ALGAL RIDGE

Location and Community Description

Good example: St. Croix—South shore

Coralline algae cements the high-energy reef crest, forming the algal ridge.

Rocky coast and offshore rock habitat types receive heavy wave action and may have algal ridge reefs associated with them. This is true of the south shore of St. Croix. Many reef crests exposed to high wave energy are cemented by species of calcareous red algae, which form the algal ridge. Algal ridges are composed largely of coralline algae (*Lithophyllum congestum* and, to a lesser extent, *Porolithon pachydermum*) and range in thickness from 20–30 centimeters up to about 1.5 meters (4 feet). The coralline algae often grow on old *Millepora* spp. and *A. palmata* colonies. *Echinometra* spp. and other boring organisms are abundant on the margins and collapsed ridge lips. The upper surface of the ridges range from mean low water to about 17 centimeters (7 inches) above that level (the maximum spring range in St. Croix is about 35 centimeters or 14 inches).

SUBSTRATE COMMUNITIES

Mud

Fine sediment, primarily of terrigenous or land-based origin, associated with discharge at the base of guts (ghuts) and buildup of organic material in areas sheltered from high-energy waves and currents at the base of large watersheds comprises this community.

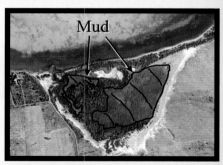

Mud

Rubble

Dead, unstable coral rubble often colonized with filamentous algae and other macroalgae in this habitat, which often occurs landward of well-developed reef formations and may be called a back reef feature.

Sand

Sand bottom is comprised of very fine to coarse carbonate sand with a few surface-living sessile organisms. These areas are

typically found exposed to currents or wave energy. The lack of habitat complexity results in a lack of fish species other than rays, which feed on mollusks and small

Diver examines a sand bottom.

NOAA Benthic Habitats map.

detritivores. Examples of this habitat type are found off north-shore beaches where winter swells prevent the establishment of seagrass beds. Sand can have a very low percentage cover of either seagrass or algae and still be mapped as sand.

Scattered Coral Rock

Sand or light rubble sub-strate with coral rock are scattered across the bottom.

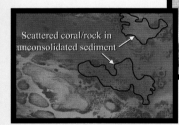

NOAA Benthic Habitats map.

Dredged

This habitat consists of excavated or dredged areas typically with sandy or muddy bottoms. There may be evidence of low-density recolonization by seagrasses or algae. Charlotte Amalie Harbor (St. Thomas), Great Cruz Bay (St. John), and Krause Lagoon (St. Croix) are good examples.

Unknown

This habitat is an unknown bottom type caused by turbidity, cloud cover, or other interference.

NOAA map 1999.

Rare Species
Sea Turtles and Seagrass

Seagrasses are flowering plants similar to those found on land that form large underwater beds on the sea bottom. Seagrasses are found in shallow coastal areas around the world. Of the 45 species worldwide, four species are found commonly in the Virgin Islands. Seagrasses are very important to our coastal environment because they help to filter sediments and improve water quality, stabilize the seafloor from wave and storm action, provide wildlife habitat, act as a food source for endangered turtles and conch and serve as a nursery area for many marine species.

Seagrass beds, a vital marine ecosystem, are disappearing at an unprecedented rate because of dredging and filling projects, soil erosion, and increased levels of water pollution, elevated salinity levels, reduced light, and boat anchoring.

Seagrass beds can be preserved by minimizing soil erosion, eliminating the dumping of sewage and toxic waste, controlling heated seawater discharges, limiting dredging and coastal development, installing permanent moorings, and eliminating anchoring in beds.

Rare sea turtles depend on healthy seagrass beds.

Introduction

Biological diversity is defined as the "the full array of life on Earth." It includes all natural communities, ecosystems, landscapes, and the individual species of plants, animals and microorganisms that inhabit these environments. Biological diversity on many scales creates an ecological web of life that is stable and resilient. As a result of human impact through habitat loss, habitat fragmentation, and pollution, the world is losing valuable biodiversity at an alarming rate, a rate never before seen on Earth. Many thousands of species—including birds, mammals, reptiles, amphibians, fishes, corals, and other invertebrates— are being threatened with extinction. Some we have never seen or classified; and others, like sea turtles, are well known. For this reason, identifying conservation priorities is crucial to targeting species and communities at risk.

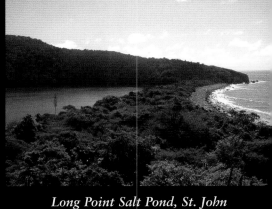

Long Point Salt Pond, St. John

Hawksnest Bay, St. John

Black mangrove habitat

Manglar islands work their way

Biodiversity Hotspots

Conservation International has identified 25 biodiversity hotspots around the world that contain 44% of all plant species and 35% of all terrestrial vertebrate species. These 25 hotspots occupy only 1.4% of the land area of the planet.

These sites have in common the fact that they shelter a great diversity of endemic species, species unique to a certain place or region and they have been significantly impacted and changed through human activities.

These hotspots are biologically diverse as a result of diverse physical and chemical environments. Variable topography, diverse ecosystems and isolation create an incubator for species diversity. Endemic species are by nature limited in distribution and threatened by local effects. Species distributions of endemics are representative of their ecological require-

*Rare wooly nipple cactus (**Mammillaria nivosa**) on a rocky headland*

ments and dispersion, yet isolation for long periods, especially on islands, allowed evolution to create unusual endemic assemblages of species, as on the Galapagos Islands.

The Philippines and Caribbean archipelagos are tropical island hotspots. Islands however, are fragile environments and many of the species lost to extinction in the last several hundred years are island species, especially birds, species of limited distribution and abundance. These species are often unable and unprepared to overcome the results of human population growth and compete with introduced or exotic species. In fact, they become easy targets.

The Saddle,
A geological fissure
at Ram Head, St. John.

Corals under red
mangrove community.

Caribbean Biodiversity Hotspot

The Caribbean region hotspot, including the islands of the Caribbean Sea, both the Greater and Lesser Antilles, and the southern third of Florida is politically, economically and ecologically diverse. It encompasses more than 260,000 square kilometers of land and 4.3 million square miles of ocean and nearshore habitat. Cuba accounts for more than 42% of the land area of the Caribbean hotspot and has 6500 plant species of which 50% are found nowhere else on earth.

Hibiscus Flower (Hibiscus rosa-sinensis)

Terrestrial Environments of the Caribbean

The Caribbean ecosystem is characterized by widely varying rainfall from island to island and across an island. The resulting vegetation systems exhibit great variability from sparse vegetation, unique wetlands, pasture and shrublands of many kinds to different types of dry and moist forest. Overlayed on a mountainous, steep and topographically diverse landscape, surrounded by the sea, these vegetation and marine environments shelter an enormous "array of life".

Bay Rum Tree (Pimenta racemosa)

Only 10% of the original vegetation remains, yet it harbors approximately 12,000 plant species, 7,000 of which are endemic for a 58% rate of endemism. There are more than 1,500 known terrestrial vertebrate species of which almost 800 are endemic. Almost 30% of mammals are endemic, 22% of the bird species and more than 84% of both reptiles and amphibians. With only a bit more than 40,000 square kilometers protected, there are about 100 threatened species, 32 critically endangered species and more than 50 species have gone extinct since 1500.

ABOVE: Caribbean Sunrise
LEFT: Hummingbird nesting

Seagrass, urchins, corals, algae, and a magnificent feather duster worm form a diverse bottom community.

Green sponge in coral community.

Lifesaving Products from Coral Reefs

Although the possible benefits from marine biotechnology applications are vast, in figures available from 1996, the U.S. only invested about $55 million. Japan, on the other hand, is spending $900 million to $1 billion per year, most of it coming from industry. Despite the low U.S. investment, 170 new patents have been filed for marine products since 1983, and almost 100 new compounds were patented between 1996 and 1999 in the U.S.

Evaluating the potential medical benefits from coral reef species takes time, money, specialized tools, and methods. Only 10% of coral reef species diversity is known. Many valuable species are rare and slow growing and they occur in limited numbers and distribution. The heavy dependence on and impact to coral reefs throughout the world has led to degradation, habitat loss, and over-exploitation, especially around population centers.

In the Bahamas, a new class of natural products called pseudopterosins are being culled from a gorgonian coral (*Pseudopterigorgia elisabethae*). This compound has both anti-inflammatory and analgesic properties and its value is currently $3 to $4 million a year.

In Japan, more than 100 species of coral reef sponges have been evaluated, and 20% were found to contain bioactive compounds.

To advance this industry, private and public organizations must address four key steps:

- Incentives to encourage partnerships in marine natural product research.
- Technical and financial resources must target species monitoring and sustainable management.
- Equitable sharing of benefits throughout the world.
- A reduction in wild harvesting and a focus on developing bioactive products from mariculture, genomic and genetic engineering.

Lifesaving Products from Coral Reefs

Marine biotechnology offers dozens of products with potential health benefits. Cancer therapy drugs now come from species of algae, and the venom of cone snails is being used as a painkiller. Anti-viral and anti-cancer drugs have been produced from extracts of Caribbean sponges. Other medicines and products are undergoing trials for treatment of leukemia, breast and liver cancers, and tumors. The marine environment is a storehouse of valuable resources, a good reason to strengthen efforts to protect, restore, and manage coral reefs before potential miracle products are lost.

Sponge, sea fan and coral community.

Marine Environments of the Caribbean

Scientist estimate that 80% of all "life forms" on Earth are found only in the ocean. Several phyla and thousands of species are found nowhere else on the planet. Coral reefs harbor diverse assemblages of corals, tunicates, molluscs, bryozoans, sponges, and echinoderms that are not rep-

Rocky coasts are an extreme environment.

resented in terrestrial systems. A small fraction of coral reef biodiversity is known and few deeper biological mysteries of these creatures lives have been discovered.

Algal community on sand.

Fire Coral has become a dominant coral on reefs.

A small hawk waits for a meal.

Little blue herons are common shore birds.

The Caribbean hotspot is a diverse marine system including some 60 species of corals and about 1,500 species of fishes, 23% of which are Caribbean endemics. Coral reefs, seagrass beds, and mangroves shelter, feed, and nurture billions of larval and adult organisms. Seagrass beds have the highest rates of primary productivity around the world and represent an important habitat within the hotspot for endangered manatees and turtles. Elkhorn coral, the primary nearshore reef builder was accimated in the last two decades by hurricanes and disease. Recent studies link terrestrial microorganisms with several coral diseases, but the link to human activities is still being investigated.

As a result of the unique structure, chemistry, and properties of marine creatures, their value in marine biotechnology—the development of new health and life-saving drugs—is growing into a tremendous business. The anti-viral drugs Ara-A and AZT and the anti-cancer agent Ara-C were developed from extracts of sponges found on Caribbean reefs. Sponges, that can regenerate from small pieces, are a promising group of organisms which have already yielded important products. In Japan, a leader in marine biotechnology, about 20% of the sponge species tested were found to contain biologically active compounds. Other products are under trial for use in treatment of breast cancer, liver cancer, tumors, and leukemia.

Waterlemon Cay, St. John with Little Thatch Cay and Tortola behind.

Seascapes, Landscapes, Biodiversity, and Humans

Coral reef ecosystems have enormous value as natural resources, with additional potential as a source of lifesaving and life-enhancing products, yet these facts are unknown to the general public and government policymakers. Unfortunately, global warming, poor and inappropriate land-use activities, commercial marine exploitation, disease, and natural catastrophes like hurricanes may eliminate these species long before we discover the miracles they hold. The place between the natural worlds of land and water is a sharing of space and blending of features that creates a unique, variable, and diverse environment. Here in the islands of the Caribbean, the influence of the sea envelops the land, creating a connected world from ridge

John's Folly Salt Pond, St. John.

Hydrocorals

COMMON NAME	SCIENTIFIC NAME
Branching fire coral	*Millepora alcicornis*
Blade fire coral	*Millepora complanata*
Rose lace coral	*Stylaster roseus*

Gorgonians

Bent sea rod	*Plexaura flexuosa*
Black sea rod	*Plexaura homomalla*
Porous sea rod	*Pseudoplexaura* spp.
Shelf-knob sea rod	*Eunicea succinea*
Warty sea rod	*Eunicea calyculata*
Slit-pore sea rod	*Plexaurella* spp.
Giant Slit-pore sea rod	*Plexaurella nutans*
Rough plume sea rod	*Muriceopsis flavida*
Sea plumes	*Pseudopterogorgia* spp.
Slimy sea plume	*Pseudopterogorgia americana*
Bipinnate sea plume	*Pseudopterogorgia bipinnata*
Common sea fan	*Gorgonia ventalina*
Venus sea fan	*Gorgonia flabellum*

Stony Corals

Staghorn coral	*Acropora cervicornis*
Fused staghorn	*Acropora prolifera*
Elkhorn coral	*Acropora palmata*
Finger coral	*Porites porites*
Mustard coral	*Porites astreoides*
Pillar coral	*Dendrogyra cylindrus*
Yellow pencil coral	*Madracis mirabilis*
Ten-ray star coral	*Madracis decactis*
Blushing star coral	*Stephanocoenia michelinii*
Boulder star coral	*Montastraea annularis*
Great star coral	*Montastraea cavernosa*
Mountainous star coral	*Montastraea faveolata*
Knobby star coral	*Solenastrea hyades*
Elliptical star coral	*Dichocoenia stokesii*
Golf ball coral	*Favia fragum*
Massive starlet coral	*Siderastrea siderea*
Lesser starlet coral	*Siderastrea radians*

Stony Corals (cont.)

COMMON NAME	SCIENTIFIC NAME
Symmetrical Brain coral	*Diploria strigosa*
Knobby brain coral	*Diploria clivosa*
Grooved brain coral	*Diploria labyrinthiformis*
Maze coral	*Meandrina meandrites*
Rose coral	*Manicina areolata*
Boulder brain coral	*Colpophyllia natans*
Lamarck's sheet coral	*Agaricia lamarcki*
Lettuce coral	*Agaricia agaricites*
Rough cactus coral	*Mycetophyllia ferox*
Sinuous cactus coral	*Isophyllia sinuosa*
Rough star coral	*Isophyllastrea rigida*
Smooth flower coral	*Eusmilia fastigiata*

Black Corals

Bushy black coral	*Antipathes* spp.
Feather black coral	*Antipathes pennacea*

Hydroids

Portuguese Man-of-War	*Physalia physalis*
Moon jelly	*Aurelia aurita*
Upside-down jellyfish	*Cassiopea frondosa*
Sea wasp	*Carybdea alata*

Anemones

Giant anemone	*Condylactis gigante*

Zoanthids

White encrusting zoanthid	*Palythoa caribaeorum*

Segmented Worms

Bearded fireworm	*Hermodice carunculata*
Magnificent feather duster	*Sabellastarte magnifica*
Christmas tree worm	*Spirobranchus giganteus*

Crustaceans

Banded coral shrimp	*Stenopus hispidus*
Golden coral shrimp	*Stenopus scutellus*
Two claw shrimp	*Brachycarpus biunguiculatus*
Caribbean spiny lobster	*Panulirus argus*
Spotted spiny lobster	*Panulirus guttatus*
Spanish lobster	*Scyllarides nodifer*
Regal slipper lobster	*Arctides guineensis*
Giant hermit crab	*Petrochirus diogenes*
Snapping shrimp	*Alpheus armatus*
Sally lightfoot	*Grapsus grapsus*
Arrow crab	*Stenorhynchus seticomis*

Mollusks

Queen conch	*Strombus gigas*
Milk conch	*Strombus costatus*
Florida horse conch	*Pleuroplaca gigantea*
Flame helmet	*Cassis flammea*
Netted olive	*Oliva reticularis*

Mollusks (cont.)

COMMON NAME	SCIENTIFIC NAME
West Indian starsnail	*Lithopoma tectum*
Stocky cerith	*Cerithium litteratum*
Flamingo tongue	*Cyphoma gibbosum*
Flat tree oyster	*Isognomon alatus*
Amber penshell	*Pinna carnea*
Sunrise tellin	*Tellina radiata*
Fuzzy chiton	*Acanthopleura granulata*
Caribbean reef squid	*Sepioteuthis sepioidea*
Common reef octopus	*Octopus briareus*
Common octopus	*Octopus vulgaris*
Lettuce sea slug	*Tridacia crispata*

Echinoderms

Cushion sea star	*Oreaster reticulatus*
Slate-pencil urchin	*Eucidaris tribuloides*
Sponge brittle star	*Ophiothrix suensonii*
Blunt-spined brittle star	*Ophiocoma echinata*
Banded-arm brittle star	*Ophioderma appressum*
Long-spined sea urchin	*Diadema antillarum*
Rock-boring urchin	*Echinometra viridis*
West Indian sea egg	*Tripneustes ventricosus*
Red heart urchin	*Moeoma ventricosa*
Sand dollar	*Clypeaster subdepressus*
Six-keyhole sand dollar	*Mellita sexiesperforata*
Donkey dung cucumber	*Holothuria mexicana*

Tunicates

Painted tunicate	*Clavelina picta*
Blue bell tunicate	*Clavelina Puerto-secensis*
Mangrove tunicate	*Ecteinascidia turbinata*

Eels, Rays and Sharks

Green moray	*Gymnothorax funebris*
Spotted moray	*Gymnothorax moringa*
Purplemouth moray	*Gymnothorax vicinus*
Southern stingray	*Dasyatis americana*
Spotted eagle ray	*Aetobatus narinari*

Eels, Rays and Sharks (cont.)

COMMON NAME	SCIENTIFIC NAME
Nurse shark	*Ginglymostoma cirratum*

Sponges

Black-ball sponge	*Ircinia strobilina*
Yellow tube sponge	*Aplysina fistularis*
Branching vase sponge	*Callyspongia vaginalis*
Loggerhead sponge	*Speciospongia vesparium*

Fishes

Too numerous to list

Marine Plants

Seagrass

Turtle grass	*Thalassia testudinum*
Manatee grass	*Syringodium filiforme*
Paddle grass	*Halpohila decipiens*
Shoal grass	*Halodule wrightii*

Brown Algae

Sargasso weed	*Sargassum natans*
Sargassum algae	*Sargassum* spp.
White-vein sargassum	*Sargassum hystrix*
Y Branched algae	*Dictyota* spp.
Serrated strap algae	*Dictyota ciliolata*
White scroll alga	*Padina jamaicencis*
Leafy rolled-blade alga	*Padina boergensenii*
Encrusting fan-leaf alga	*Lobophora variegata*
Saucer leaf alga	*Turbinaria tricostata*
Blistered saucer leaf	*Turbinaria turbinata*

Green Algae

Watercress alga	*Halimeda opuntia*
Large leaf watercress	*Halimeda discoidea*
Stalked lettuce leaf	*Halimeda tuna*
Small-leaf hanging vine	*Halimeda goreaui*
Flat-top bristle brush	*Penicillus pyriformis*
Bristle ball brush	*Penicillus dumetosus*
Green feather alga	*Caulerpa sertularioides*
Green grape alga	*Caulerpa racemosa*
Sea pearl	*Ventricaria ventricosa*
Elongated sea pearls	*Valonia macrophysa*
Saucer blade alga	*Avrainvillea asarifolia*
Mermaid's fans	*Udotea* spp.
Pinecone alga	*Rhipocephalus phoenix*
Mermaid's wine glass	*Acetabularia calyculus*

Red Algae

Tubular thicket algae	*Galaxaura* spp.
Crustose coralline algae	*Porlithon* spp.

I = Introduced   R = Rare   P = Protected by VI Law   E = Federally Endangered

(*Andira inermis*
hog turd)

Moist Forests

EMERGENT *(trees above the main canopy layer)*
and MAIN LAYER (trees)
Buchenavia tetraphylla
Bucida buceras - gris gris, black olive
Ceiba pentandra - kapok, silk cotton
Ficus citrifolia - white fig
Ficus trigonata - wild ficus, strangler fig
Hura crepitans - sandbox tree
Hymenaea courbaril - locust tree
Manilkara bidentata - bullet wood - R
Melicoccus bijugatus - genip - I
Roystonea borinquena - cabbage palm, royal palm
Sapium caribaeum - milktree - R
Spondias mombin - hog plum
Swietenia mahagoni - mahogany - I
Terminalia catappa - W.I. almond - I

MAIN and MIDDLE LAYER (trees)
Acacia muricata - amaret
Adenanthera pavonina - jumbee bead - I
Andira inermis - hog turd
Ardisia obovata - breakbill
Byrsonima spicata
Calyptranthes thomasiana - St. Thomas lid flower - E
Capparis amplissima - caper
Casearia guianensis - wild coffee
Cassia nitida
Chrysophyllum pauciflorum - palmet
Clusia rosea - autograph tree
Coccothrinax alta - teyer palm
Cocos nucifera - coconut - I
Cordia collococca - red manjack
Cordia sulcata - white manjack
Cordia laevigata - W.I. cherry
Cordia alliodora - Copper
Cyathea arborea - tree fern - R
Erythrina eggersii - Egger's cockspur - P
Eugenia axillaris
Eugenia biflora
Eugenia confusa
Eugenia monticola
Eugenia pseudopsidium - wild guava
Eugenia rhombea - cranberry
Guapira fragrans - black mampoo
Guazuma ulmifolia - W.I. elm
Guettarda odorata - blackcherry

Guettarda scabra - green heart - R
Ilex urbaniana - R
Inga laurina - lady finger tree, sweet pea
Mammea americana - mammee apple
Mangifera indica - mango - I
Margaritaria nobilis - gonglehout
Maytenus laevigata
Melicoccus bijugatus - genip - I
Miconia laevigata
Morinda citrifolia - I
Myrcia citrifolia
Myrcianthes fragrans - spice guava - R
Myrciaria floribunda - guavaberry
Ocotea floribunda
Ocotea coriacea - pepper cillament
Pimenta racemosa - bay rum
Samanea saman - rain tree - I
Sideroxylon foetidissimum - bully, bully mastic - R
Tabebuia heterophylla - pink cedar
Ternstroemia peduncularis - R
Tetrazygia angustifolia - sprat wood, stinking fish - R
Tetrazygia eleagnoides - kre kre
Thespesia populnea - cork wood, heiti heiti - I
Vitex divaricata - R
Zanthoxylum flavum - yellowheart - R
Zanthoxylum martinicense
Zanthoxylum monophyllum - yellow prickle

MIDDLE and LOWER LAYER (shrubs, lianas/vines)
Buxus vahlii - shrub - E
Cassia nitida - shrub
Celtis iguanaea - cat's claw, cockspur vine
Cestrum laurifolium - shrub
Chionanthus compacta - shrub
Cissampelos pariera - velvet leaf vine
Dioscorea alata - red yam, yam vine
Dioscorea pilosiuscula - vine
Epipremnum aureum - pothos, devil's vine - I
Eugenia procera - shrub
Eugenia pseudopsidium - wild guava - shrub
Faramea occidentalis - wild coffee - shrub
Gonzalagunia hirsuta - shrub
Ipomea hederifolia - sweet William - vine
Ixora ferrea - shrub
Lepianthes peltatum - motherbush - shrub
Macfadyena unguis-cati - cat's claw - vine
Palicourea croceoides - yellow cedar - shrub
Passiflora spp. - passionflower - vines
Philodendron scandens - philodendron - vine - I
Piper amalago - black wattle - shrub
Pisonia aculeata - prickly mampoo - liana
Psychotria spp. - shrubs
Smilax coriacea - vine
Stigmaphyllon emarginatum - black wiss - liana
Stigmaphyllon floribundum - bull wiss - liana
Tournefortia hirsutissima - chiggernit - vine
Trichostigma octandrum - basket wiss, hoop vine - liana

GROUND LAYER

Adiantum fragile - maidenhair fern
Anthurium spp. - wild anthurium - herbs
Blechum occidentale - fern
Nephrolepis spp.- ferns
Olyra latifolia - grass
Peperomia glabella - herb
Peperomia humilis - herb
Peperomia magnoliifolia - herb
Peperomia myrtifolia - shiny bush - herb
Polypodium spp. - ferns
Pteris biaurita - fern
Thelypteris spp. - ferns

(Poitea florida
wattapama)

Dry Forests

EMERGENT and MAIN LAYER (trees)

Acacia muricata - amaret
Acacia tortuosa - casha
Amyris elemifera - torchwood, candle wood
Bourreria succulenta - pigeon berry
Bucida buceras - gris gris, black olive
Bursera simaruba - turpentine, gumbo limbo
Capparis amplissima - caper
Capparis indica -linguam
Capparis cynophallophora - black willy, linguam
Cassine xylocarpa - marble tree
Citharexylum fruticosum - fiddlewood
Clusea rosea - autograph tree
Coccoloba diversifolia - doveplum
Coccoloba microstachya - puckout
Coccoloba uvifera - sea grape
Colubrina arborescens - coffee colubrina, maubi
Colubrina elliptica - maubi
Cordia rickseckeri - black manjack
Erithalis fruticosa - black torch
Eugenia biflora
Eugenia monticola
Ficus citrifolia - white fig
Guapira fragrans - mampoo
Guettarda scabra - green heart
Guettarda odorata - blackberry
Krugiodendron ferreum - ironwood, ebony, guatafer
Maytenus laevigata
Melicoccus bijugatus - genip - **I**
Myrciaria floribunda - guavaberry
Ocotea coriacea - pepper cillament
Pimenta racemosa - bay rum
Piscidia carthagenensis - fish poison

Pisonia subcordata - water mampoo
Pithecellobium unguis-cati - black bead, bread & cheese
Plumeria alba - wild frangipani
Sideroxylon salicifolium
Swietenia mahagoni - mahogany - **I**
Tabebuia heterophylla - pink cedar
Zanthoxylum flavum - yellow sandalwood - **R**
Zanthoxylum martinicense
Zanthoxylum thomasianum - St. Thomas prickly ash - **E**

MIDDLE and LOWER LAYER (trees, shrubs, lianas/ vines)

Acacia riparia - catch and keep - liana
Argythamnia spp.- shrubs
Comocladia dodonaea - Christmas bush, pra pra - shrub
Crossopetalum rhacoma - shrub
Croton spp. - maran - shrubs
Erythroxylum brevipes -brisselet - shrub
Eugenia cordata - shrub
Euphorbia petiolaris - black manchineel - shrub
Forestiera eggersiana - shrub
Hylocereus trigonatus - nightblooming cereus - liana
Ipomoea steudelii - vine
Jacquinia arborea - barbasco - shrub, tree
Jacquinia berterii - barbasco - shrub, tree
Lantana spp. - lantana - shrubs
Leucaena leucocephala - tan tan, wild tamarind - shrub - **I**
Neea buxifolia - **R**
Oplonia spinosa - shrub
Pictetia aculeata - fustic
Poitea florida - soldier whip, wattapama - shrub, tree
Samyda dodecandra - shrub
Savia sessiliflora - shrub
Schaefferia frutescens - boxwood - shrub
Sideroxylon obovatum - shrub, tree
Solanum spp. - shrubs
Tragia volubilis - stinging nettle, cow itch - vine

GROUND LAYER

Anthurium cordatum - wild anthurium - herb
Anthurium crenatum - rat tail, soapy soapy - herb
Brassavola cucullata - orchid - **P**
Bromelia pinguin - pinguin, wild pineapple - **I**
Callisia repens - inch plant - herb
Canavalia maritima - beach pea - vine
Celosia nitida - herb
Commelina erecta - French grass - herb
Epidendrum ciliare - Christmas orchid - **P**
Ipomoea pes-caprae - beach morning glory - vine
Justicia spp. - herbs
Lasiacis divaricata - grass
Peperomia spp. - herbs
Portulaca oleracea - pussly, purslane - herb
Psychillis macconnelliae - orchid - **P**
Scleria lithosperma - grass-like sedge
Stigmaphyllon emarginatum - black wiss - liana
Talinum triangulare - herb
Tetramicra canliculata - orchid - **P**
Tillandsia lineatispica - herb - **R**
Tillandsia utriculata - wild pin, air plant - herb
Wedelia fruticosa - wild creeping daisy - herb

I = Introduced   R = Rare   P = Protected by VI Law   E = Federally Endangered

(*Capparis flexuosa* limber caper)

Commelina erecta - French grass - herb
Eragrostis spp. - grasses
Hymenocallis caribaea - lady bug, white lily - herb
Paspalum maxum - grass
Rivina humilis - jumbeepepper - herb
Talinum paniculatum - talinum - herb
Tragia volubilis - stinging nettle - vine

Woodlands

MAIN LAYER (trees, palms)
Acacia macracantha - stink casha
Amyris elemifera - torchwood
Bursera simaruba - turpentine, gumbo limbo
Capparis cynophallophora - black willy, linguam
Cassine xylocarpa - marble tree
Coccoloba uvifera - sea grape
Cocos nucifera - coconut - I
Cocothrinax alta - teyer palm
Conocarpus erectus - buttonwood
Erithalis fruticosa - black torch
Eugenia biflora
Eugenia foetida
Guapira fragrans - black mampoo
Hippomane mancinella - manchineel
Jacquinia arborea - barbasco
Jacquinia berterii - barbasco
Laguncularia racemosa - white mangrove - P
Morinda citrifolia - pain killer - I
Pisonia subcordata - water mampoo
Plumeria alba - wild frangipani
Randia aculeata - inkberry
Sabal causiarum - P.R. hat palm - I
Thespesia populnea - heiti heiti, cork wood

MIDDLE LAYER (shrubs, lianas/vines)
Caesalpinia bonduc - nickers - shrub
Capparis flexuosa - limber caper - shrub
Chamaesyce articulata - shrub
Cissus trifoliata - sorrel vine - vine
Cissus sicyoides - pudding wiss - vine
Crossopetalum rhacoma - shrub
Croton betulinus - broom bush - shrub
Dendropemom caribaeus - mistletoe - parasitic shrub
Helicteres jamaicensis - cat's balls, cow bush - shrub
Lantana involucrata - wild sage - shrub
Oplonia spinosa - shrub
Passiflora suberosa - indigo or ink berry - vine
Prestonia agglutinata - vine
Psychotria nervosa - shrub
Smilax coriacea - vine
Stigmaphyllon emarginatum - black wiss - vine
Tournefortia microphylla - vine

GROUND LAYER
Callisia repens - inch plant - herb
Celosia nitida - herb

Shrublands

MAIN LAYER (trees)
Acacia muricata - amarat
Acacia tortuosa - casha
Acacia macracantha - stink casha
Avicennia germinans - black mangrove - P
Bursera simaruba - turpentine tree
Cassine xylocarpa - marble tree
Coccoloba uvifera - sea grape
Conocarpus erectus - buttonwood
Cordia dentata - flute boom, white manjack
Erithalis fruticosa - black torch
Ficus citrifolia - white fig
Hippomane mancinella - manchineel
Jacquinia berterii - barbasco
Jacquinia arborea - barbasco
Leucaena leucocephala - tan tan, wild tamarind - I
Piscidia carthagenensis - fish poison
Pisonia subcordata - water mampoo, loblolly
Pithecellobium unguis-cati - bread and cheese
Schaefferia frutescens - boxwood
Tabebuia heterophylla - pink cedar
Tecoma stans - ginger thomas, yellow cedar - I
Thespesia populnea - heiti heiti
Zanthoxylum thomasianum - St. Thomas prickly ash - E

MIDDLE and GROUND LAYER S(shrubs, cacti, succulents, orchids, etc.)
Agave eggersiana - succulent - R
Agave missionum - century plant - succulent
Argusia gnaphalodes - black tea, bay lavender - shrub
Baccharis dioica - saltbush - shrub
Borrichia arborescens - bay marigold - shrub
Brunfelsia americana - rain tree - shrub
Byrsonima lucida - guanaberry - shrub
Chromolaena corymbosum - shrub
Comocladia dodonaea - christmas bush - shrub
Crossopetalum rhacoma - poison cherry - shrub
Croton spp.- maran, white marang - shrub
Croton flavens - maran, yellow marang - shrub
Epidendrum ciliare - Christmas orchid - P
Ernodea littoralis - ernodea - shrub
Gymnanthes lucida - crab wood, goat wood - shrub
Hylocereus trigonus - night-blooming cereus
Machaonia woodburyana - R
Melocactus intortus - turk's cap - cactus - P
Oplonia spinosa - shrub

Oplonia microphylla - shrub
Opuntia repens - suckers - cactus - P
Opuntia dillenii - miss blyden, prickly pear - cactus - P
Opuntia rubescens - blyden bush, prickly pear - cactus - P
Pilosocereus royenii - pipe organ - cactus - P
Piptocoma antillana - shrub
Rochefortia acanthophora - shrub
Scaevola plumieri - scaevola - shrub
Stenocereus peruvianus - cactus - P
Suriana maritima- bay cedar - shrub
Tetramicra canaliculata - grass orchid - orchid - P
Tolumnia prionochila - dancing lady - orchid - P
Urochloa maximum - guinea grass - I
Vanilla barbellata - Vanilla - orchid - P
Wedelia fruticosa - wild wedelia - subshrub

(*Croton astroites* maran)

Herbaceous/Grasslands

TREES
Acacia spp. - casha
Bursera simarouba - turpentine, gumbo limbo
Cordia ricksekerii - orange manjack
Cordia alba - white manjack
Eugenia monticola
Guapira fragrans - mampoo
Mangifera indica - mango - I
Pictetia aculeata - fustic
Psidium guajava - guava - I
Tabebuia heterophylla - pink cedar

MIDDLE LAYER (shrubs, cacti, vines)
Cordia polycephala - shrub
Croton spp. - maran - shrubs
Ipomoea tiliacea - willy vine
Lantana camara - wild sage - shrub
Lantana urticifolia - shrub
Melocactus intortus - turk's cap - cactus - P
Pilosocereus royenii - pipe organ - cactus - P
Ricinis communis - castor bean - I

GROUND LAYER
Arthrostylidium farctum - grass
Bothriochloa pertusa - hurricane grass
Chloris barbata - grass
Cynodon dactylon - Bermuda grass
Digitaria spp. - grass
Echinochloa colona - grass
Eleusine indica - Dutch grass
Eriochloa punctata - grass
Setaria setosa - grass
Talinum triangulare - herb
Urichloa maxima - guinea grass - I

(*Typha domingensis* Cattails)

Wetlands

MANGROVES, SWAMPS, SALT FLATS AND SALT PONDS

UPPER LAYER (trees)
Annona glabra - swamp apple
Avicennia germinans - black mangrove - P
Bontia daphnoides - white alling
Conocarpus erectus - buttonwood
Hippomane mancinella - manchineel
Laguncularia racemosa - white mangrove - P
Machaerium lunatum
Rhizophora mangle - red mangrove - P

MIDDLE LAYER (shrubs, vines)
Acrostichum danaefolium - swamp fern
Caesalpinia bonduc - gray nickers - shrub
Chrysobalanus icaco - cocoplum
Croton discolor - maran, goat climax - shrub
Dalbergia ecastaphyllum - coin plant
Sesbania sericea - shrub
Stigmaphyllon emarginatum - black wiss - liana
Suriana maritima - bay cedar

GROUND LAYER
Alternanthera philoxeroides - herb
Amaranthus crassipes - herb
Bacopa monnieri - herb of grace - herb
Batis maritima - saltwort or turtleweed - herb
Blutaparon vermiculare - lumboo, whitey mary - herb
Chamaesyce spp. - herbs, subshrubs
Cypselia humifusa - herb - R
Heliotropium curassavicum - salt heliotrope - herb
Portulaca spp.- herbs
Sesuvium portulacastrum - sea purslane - herb
Sporobolus virginus - beachgrass - grass
FRESH WATER PONDS

BORDER PLANTS
Acrostichum danaefolium - swamp fern
Canna indica - canna, wild arrowroot - herb - I
Colocasia esculenta - dasheen, coco yam, taro - herb - I
Cyperus spp. - grass-like sedges
Eriochloa punctata - grass
Ludwigia octovalvis - Mexican primrose - subshrub
Maranta arundinacea - maranta, arrowroot - I
Typha domingensis - cattails

AQUATIC PLANTS
Eichhornia crassipes - water hyacinth - I
Lemna aequinoctialis - lesser duckweed
Neptunia plena - water dead and awake
Nymphaea spp. - I
Pistia stratiotes - water lettuce - I

Acevedo-Rodriguez, Pedro. 1996. Flora of St. John. Memoirs of the New York Botanical Garden, Vol. 78. Bronx, NY: The New York Botanical Garden.

Adjei, Martin, and Olasee Davis. 1999. Pasture Brush Weed Control in the Virgin Islands. Farmers Bulletin, No. 3. St. Croix: UVI.

Arendt, Randall G. 1996. Conservation Design for Subdivisions. Natural Lands Trust. Washington, DC: Island Press.

Brewer, David. 2004. Personal Communication. St. Thomas, USVI.

Booker, John, et al. 1998. Mangroves [online]. Florida: Seacamp Association, Inc. Web: (http://mangroves+%26+Seacamp+Association+Inc.)

Colon-Dieppa, Elroy, et. al. 1988-89. U.S. Virgin Islands Floods and Droughts. National Water Summary. U.S. Geological Survey. San Juan, PR. 521-526.

Devine, Barry, et al. 2003. Coral Bay Sediment Deposition and Reef Assessment Study. Proceedings of the NonPoint Source Pollution Symposium. St. Thomas, USVI.

Drayton, Nicolas, et al. 2005. The State of the Coral Reefs of the Virgin Islands. The Ocean Conservancy. Washington, DC.

Federal Geographic Data Committee Secretariat. 1997. Vegetation Classification and Information Standards. FGDC-STD-005. Reston,VA.
Web address: http://www.fgdc.gov/Standards/Documents/Standards/Vegetation.

Gibney, Eleanor, et al. 1999. USVI Vegetation Classification System. (Unpublished manuscript for The Nature Conservancy.) St. John, USVI.

Hanlon, Roger, Federick Bayer, and Gilbert Voss. 1975. Guide to the Mangroves, Buttonwood, and Poisonous Shoreline Trees of Florida, the Gulf of Mexico, and the Caribbean Region. Miami, FL: University of Florida Sea Grant Program.

Jarecki, Lianna. 1999. A Review of Salt Pond Ecosystems. Proceedings of the NonPoint Source Pollution Symposium. St. Thomas, USVI.

Johnston, Barbara R. 1983. Cultural Ecology at Magens Bay. (Publication draft.) VI Planning Office, Division for Archaeology and Historic Preservation. St. Thomas, USVI.

Lindsay, Kevel, and Bruce Horwith. 1997. A Vegetation Classification of Antigua - Barbuda - Redonda. Eastern Caribbean Biodiversity Programme, Biodiversity Publication #2. Island Resources Foundation. Washington DC.

Lugo, Ariel E. 2002. Caribbean Landscapes in Turmoil [online]. Puerto Rico: USDA Forest Service, Institute of Tropical Forestry. Web address: .http://gsa.confex.com/gsa/2002AM/final-program/abstract_41005.htm.

Lundberg, Emily. 1997. Background for the Teaching of Caribbean Prehistory. Dept. of Conservation and Cultural Affairs, St. Thomas, USVI.

Margaret Hayes. 2003. Personal communication. St. Croix, USVI.

National Oceanic and Atmospheric Administration. 2001. Benthic Habitats Classification for Puerto Rico and the Virgin Islands. Washington D.C.

Nellis, David W., and Arthur E. Dammann. 1992. A Natural History Atlas to the Cays of the U.S. Virgin Islands. Sarasota, FL. Pineapple Press, Inc.

Rogers, Caroline S., and Robert Teytaud. 1988. Marine and Terrestrial Ecosystems of the Virgin Islands National Park and Biosphere Reserve. Virgin Islands Resource Management Cooperative, Virgin Islands National Park, and Island Resources Foundation. Wash. DC.

Rudy O'Reilly. 2003. Natural Resources Conservation Service. Personal communication. St. Croix, USVI.

Scatena, F.N. 1992-93. Watershed Research. Institute of Tropical Forestry Annual Letter. USDA Forest Service. Rio Piedras, PR. 39-42.

Stein, Bruce A., Lynn S. Kutner, and Jonathan S. Adams, eds. 2000. Precious Heritage - The Status of Biodiversity in the United States. The Nature Conservancy. NY: Oxford Univiversity Press.

Stengel, Carolyn A. 1998. The Survey of the Salt Ponds of the U.S. Virgin Islands. (Unpublished final report.) VI Division of Fish and Wildlife Service. USVI.

The Ocean Conservancy. 2003. Cruising in Paradise. Washington D.C.

Thomas, Toni. 1993. Idrena Henderson Interview Transcript. (Typewritten manuscript.) University Virgin Islands, St. Thomas, USVI.

Torres-Sierra, H., and T. Rodriguez-Alonso. 1987. Water Supply and Use: U.S. Virgin Islands. National Water Summary. U.S. Geological Survey. San Juan, PR. 485-490.

University of Wisconsin Botany Course 422. Tropical Dry Forests and Savannas [online]. Web address: www.botany.wisc.edu/courses/botany_422/Lecture/Let08TropD,[Tropical Dry Forests and Savannas)

U.S. Fish & Wildlife Service. Caribbean Freshwater Crustaceans. U.S. Fish & Wildlife Service Factsheet. Boqueron, PR.

U.S. Fish & Wildlife Service. Caribbean River Fish. U.S. Fish & Wildlife Service Factsheet. Boqueron, PR.

University of Puerto Rico. 2001. Guide to Identify Common Wetland Plants in the Caribbean Area: Puerto Rico and the U.S. Virgin Islands. San Juan, PR: University of Puerto Rico Press.

V.I. Dept. of Conservation and Cultural Affairs. 1979. Environmental Laws and Regulations of the Virgin Islands. Oxford, NH: Equity Publishing Corporation.

Watlington, Roy. 2003. Personal Communication. St. Thomas, USVI.

Welsh, David. 1992. Riparian Forest Buffers. Rachor, PA: USDA Forest Service.

Woodbury, Roy O., and Peter Weaver. 1984. The Vegetation of St. John and Hassel Island, U.S. Virgin Islands. (Unpublished manuscript.) St. John, USVI.

Wright, Julie. 2002. Virgin Islands Environment Protection Handbook 2002. St. Thomas, USVI: UVI Cooperative Extension Service.

Wright, Julie. 1994. Watershed Awareness. (Trifold brochure.) UVI Cooperative Extension Service. St. Thomas, USVI. Express Press.